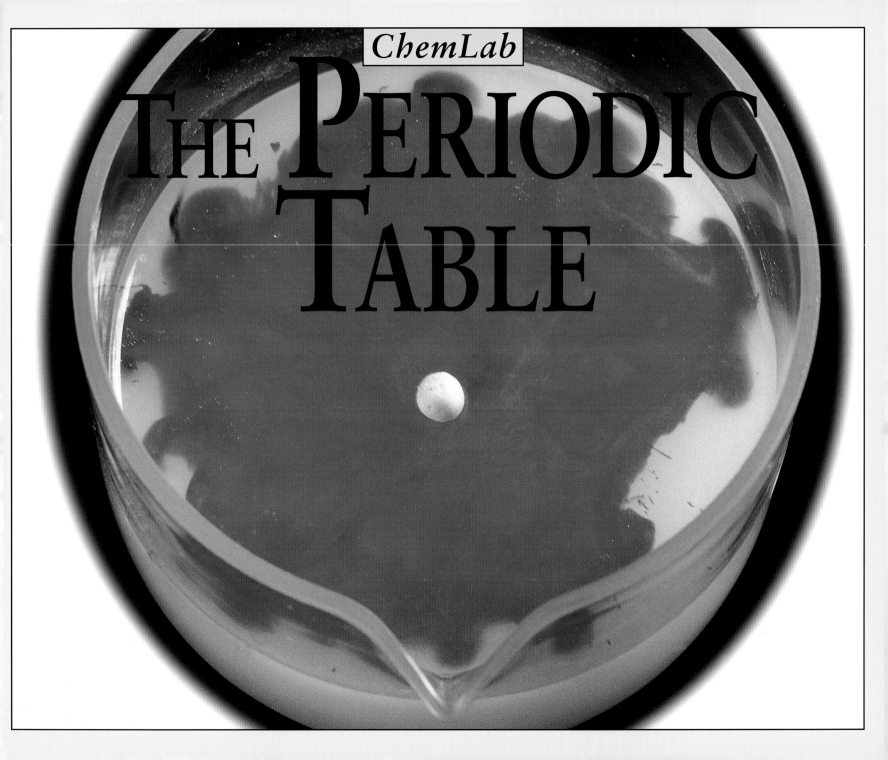

ChemLab

THE PERIODIC TABLE

Atlantic Europe Publishing

First published in 1998 by Atlantic Europe Publishing
Company Limited, Greys Court Farm, Greys Court,
Henley-on-Thames, Oxon, RG9 4PG, UK.

Author
Brian Knapp, BSc, PhD
Project consultant
*Keith B. Walshaw, MA, BSc, DPhil
(Head of Chemistry, Leighton Park School)*
Project Director
Duncan McCrae, BSc
Editor
Mary Sanders, BSc
Special photography
Ian Gledhill
Illustrations
David Woodroffe
Designed and produced by
EARTHSCAPE EDITIONS
Print consultants
Chromo Litho Ltd
Reproduced in Malaysia by
Global Colour
Printed and bound in Italy by
L.E.G.O. SpA

Suggested cataloguing location
Knapp, Brian
    The Periodic Table
    ISBN 1 869860 32 2
    – ChemLab series, volume 3
540

Picture credits
All photographs are from the **Earthscape
Editions** photolibrary except the
following:
(c=centre t=top b=bottom l=left r=right)
Mary Evans Picture Library 6tr, 7tr;
by kind permission of **Vauxhall Motors
Limited** 33tr; by kind permission of
Rolls-Royce plc 37tl

*This product is manufactured from sustainable
managed forests. For every tree cut down at
least one more is planted.*

Contents

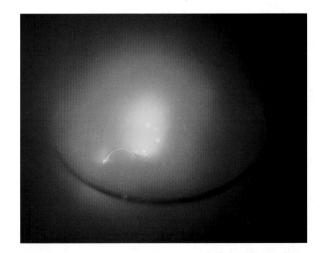

HOW TO USE THIS BOOK

These two pages show you how to get the most from this book.

❶ THE CONTENTS

Use the table of contents to see how this book is divided into themes. Each theme may have one or more demonstrations.

❷ THEMES

Each theme begins with a theory section on yellow-coloured paper. Major themes may contain several pages of theory for the demonstrations that are presented on the subsequent pages. They also contain biographies of scientists, whose work was important in the understanding of the theme.

❸ DEMONSTRATIONS

Demonstrations are at the heart of any chemistry study. However, many demonstrations cannot easily be shown to a whole class for health and safety reasons, because the demonstration requires a close-up view, because it is over too quickly, takes too long to complete, or because it requires special apparatus. The demonstrations shown here have been photographed especially to overcome these problems and give you a very close-up view of the key stages in each reaction.

The text, pictures and diagrams are closely connected. To get the best from the demonstration, look closely at each picture as soon as its reference occurs in the text.

Many of the pictures show enlarged views of parts of the demonstration to help you see exactly what is happening. Notice, too, that most pictures form part of a sequence. You will find that it pays to look at the picture sequence more than once, and always be careful to make sure you can see exactly what is described in any picture before you move on.

The main heading for a demonstration or a set of demonstrations.

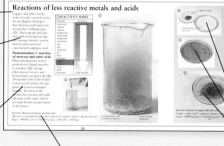

An introduction expands on the heading, summarising the demonstration or group of demonstrations and their context in the theme.

Each demonstration is carefully explained and illustrated with photographs and, where necessary, with diagrams, tables and graphs. The illustrations referred to are numbered ①, ②, ③, etc.

Chemical equations are shown where appropriate (see the explanation of equations at the bottom of page 5).

The photographs show the key stages that you might see if you witness a demonstration at first-hand. Examine them very carefully against the text description.

APPARATUS

The demonstrations have been carefully conducted as representative examples of the main chemical processes. The apparatus used is standard, but other choices are possible and you may see different equipment in your laboratory, so make sure you understand the principles behind the apparatus selected. The key pieces of apparatus are defined in the glossary.

❹ GLOSSARY OF TECHNICAL TERMS

Words with which you may be unfamiliar are shown in small capitals where they first occur in the text. Use the glossary on pages 66–74 to find more information about these technical words. Over 400 items are presented alphabetically.

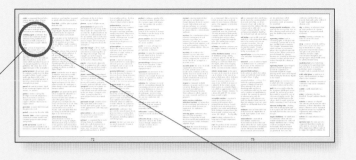

oxidising agent: a substance that removes electrons from another substance being oxidised (and therefore is itself reduced) in a redox reaction. *Example:* chlorine (Cl_2).

❺ INDEX TO ALL VOLUMES IN THE SET

To look for key words in any of the 12 volumes that make up the ChemLab set, use the Master Index on pages 75 to 80. The instructions on page 75 show you how to cross-reference between volumes.

The most important locations of the term 'oxidising agent' are given in a master index which includes references to all of the volumes in the ChemLab set.

ABBREVIATIONS

Units are in the international metric system. Some units of measurement are abbreviated, or shortened, as follows:
°C = degrees Celsius
km = kilometre
m = metre
cm = centimetre
mm = millimetre
sq m = square metre
g = gram
kg = kilogram
kJ = kilojoule
l = litre

❻ CHEMICAL EQUATIONS

Important or relevant chemical equations are shown in written and symbolic form together with additional information.

What the reaction equation illustrates

Where relevant, the oxidation state is shown as Roman numerals in brackets.

Word equation

EQUATION: Reaction of copper and nitric acid

Copper + nitric acid ⇨ *copper(II) nitrate + water + nitrogen dioxide*

Symbol equation
The symbols for each element can be found in any Periodic Table.

$Cu(s) + 4HNO_3(conc) \rightrightarrows Cu(NO_3)_2(aq) + 2H_2O(l) + 2NO_2(g)$

Blue

The symbol indicating the state of each substance is shown as follows:
(*s*) = solid
(*g*) = gaseous
(*l*) = liquid
(*aq*) = aqueous
(*conc*) = concentrated

The two halves of the chemical equation are separated by the arrow that shows the progression of the reaction. Each side of the equation must balance.

Sometimes additional descriptions are given below the symbol equation.

The correct number of atoms, ions and molecules and their proportions in any compound are shown by the numbers. A free electron is shown as an e^-.

THE PERIODIC LAW

The Periodic Law is a fundamental principle in chemistry which enables chemists to understand what would otherwise be a bewildering array of elements.

The Periodic Law states that chemical ELEMENTS, when arranged in order of increasing ATOMIC NUMBER to form a chart (the PERIODIC TABLE), show repeating (periodic) properties.

The atomic number is the number of PROTONS in the nucleus of an ATOM. This, in turn, is equal to the number of ELECTRONS surrounding the nucleus.

The history of the Periodic Table

The Periodic Table was first described by a Russian teacher, Dmitri Ivanovich Mendeleev between 1869 and 1870. He was interested in writing a chemistry textbook, and wanted to show his students that there were certain patterns in the elements. So he set out the elements (of which only 57 were known at the time) using their known properties. On the assumption that there was a pattern to the elements, he left blank spaces where elements seemed to be missing. Using this first version of the Periodic Table, he was able to predict, in detail, the chemical and physical properties of elements that had not yet been discovered. As soon as scientists looked for the missing elements, using the clues provided by Mendeleev's table, they soon began to find them.

The only element that Mendeleev could not fit into his scheme was hydrogen, so he placed it in a box

GREAT EXPERIMENTAL SCIENTISTS
Dmitri Ivanovich Mendeleev

Dmitri Ivanovich Mendeleev (1834–1907) was born in Siberia but moved to St Petersburg to do his university degrees. He was professor of chemistry there from 1867.

Mendeleev was convinced that the order to the elements lay in their ATOMIC WEIGHTS and when he arranged them in the sequence of increasing atomic weights, he noted that the chemical properties of the elements were grouped into, already familiar, families.

By doing this, he discovered that he had to leave spaces in his table (there were only 57 elements known at that time) and that he could predict the properties of the elements that should occupy the spaces. As the elements gallium, scandium and germanium were discovered, and their properties found to fit exactly in the spaces predicted, the Periodic Table of Mendeleev was accepted and quickly became one of the cornerstones of chemistry.

The Periodic Table showed scientists where to look to discover new elements. On this basis, scientists such as William Ramsay found the inert gases, xenon and krypton. Similarly, the radioactive elements were mainly found with the aid of the Periodic Table.

Mendeleev did not have a theory to explain the table he had constructed; that had to wait for the atomic structure of atoms to be worked out in the 20th century.

on its own. Otherwise, the elements were all placed in order, horizontally.

When an element was reached with properties similar to the first one in the top row, a new row was started. By following this rule, similarities among the elements could be found by reading up and down the table. By reading across the rows, the elements were seen to increase in atomic number.

This was the foundation of the Periodic Table we use today (see pages 10 and 11).

The elements, electrons and chemical reactions

The electrons that are present in an atom are found at different energy levels. Sets of electrons with similar energy characteristics are called 'SHELLS'. The chemical properties of an element depend on the number of electrons in the outermost shell (region) of the atom.

In chemistry, these shells can be drawn as circles around the nucleus to make a shell diagram. The number of electrons in each shell can be written on each circle as shown in this book (①), or represented by dots. The arrangement of the electrons in an atom is called the ELECTRON CONFIGURATION.

The first shell can hold two electrons, the second shell can contain eight, the third 18, and so on. The total number of electrons is represented by the atomic number, which is shown for each element on the Periodic Table on pages 10 and 11. The shell diagrams for each element are also shown in the following pages of this book.

Atoms can form compounds by sharing some of the electrons in their outermost shells (this is called COVALENT BONDING). Atoms may also lose or gain electrons to form charged particles (IONS). Oppositely charged ions attract one another and so can form IONIC COMPOUNDS.

Atoms of the NOBLE GASES, such as helium and argon, have a full outer shell and so are unreactive or inert, whereas atoms with an incomplete outer shell are reactive. Chlorine, for example, contains only seven electrons in its outer shell (i.e. it is one electron

---

① **SHELL DIAGRAMS**

(Below) An argon atom (Ar) has an atomic number of 18 and therefore has 18 electrons that can be arranged as shown in this shell diagram.

(Below) A chlorine atom (Cl) has an atomic number of 17 and therefore has 17 electrons that can be arranged as shown in this shell diagram.

The outer shell is full and so this atom does not react – it is inert.

The outer shell has seven instead of eight electrons and so this atom is highly reactive, being strongly attractive to an electron.

Number of electrons in each shell

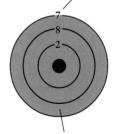

Shell

The nucleus at the centre of the atom contains protons and neutrons. The number of protons is given by the atomic number, more recently called the PROTON NUMBER.

The background colour shows whether the element is a metal, non-metal or metalloid. The Periodic Table on page 11 shows a colour key.

short of a full set) and so is very reactive. Some metals are also reactive because of their incomplete shells. Sodium, for example, has an outer shell containing only one electron (i.e. one more than a full set).

Radioactive elements differ from non-radioactive elements in that they lose particles from their nucleus (they DECAY) as well as losing electrons from their surrounding shells. As a result, their atomic number changes and they become new elements. Nuclear reactions are generally not carried out in school or college laboratories, so they are not discussed further in this book.

Groups and periods

In the Periodic Table, the elements are arranged in order of increasing atomic (proton) number in 'GROUPS' (columns) and 'PERIODS' (rows) (see pages 10 and 11).

There are eight groups (or columns) of elements, which are referred to as Groups 1 to 8. The number of the group represents the number of electrons in the outer shell of the atoms of the elements in that group. For example, neon and argon have a full set of eight electrons in their outer shell and so belong to Group 8. Sodium has only one electron in its outer shell and so like potassium belongs to Group 1, and so on.

The TRANSITION METALS, make up the region, or BLOCK, between Groups 2 and 3. These elements are unusual in that their properties depend on the number of electrons in the shell one in from the outside (the penultimate shell).

Sir William Ramsay

Sir William Ramsay (1852–1916) was a British chemist born in Glasgow, Scotland, who discovered and isolated the inert gases of the atmosphere and placed them in the Periodic System. In 1887 he became professor of chemistry at London University. He received the 1904 Nobel Prize in chemistry for his work on the noble gases.

In 1892 another chemist, Lord Rayleigh, discovered that the density of nitrogen prepared from chemicals was not the same as that of the nitrogen extracted from air. Ramsay was able to extract both oxygen and nitrogen from the air, and in doing this he found he was left with an unknown gas, which proved to be argon. Using the Periodic Table, Ramsay predicted that argon and helium would be members of a family of at least three more elements. Subsequently, he extracted the three unknown gases: neon, krypton, and xenon. He later also discovered radon.

As we move along each period (or row) in the Periodic Table, the atomic number of the elements increases by 1. This corresponds to an additional proton and electron. Moving down the table, each new period corresponds to a new outer shell of electrons around the nucleus. Hence, hydrogen (H, atomic number 1), the first element in the first period, has one electron in the first shell, and helium (He, atomic number 2), the last element in period 1, has two electrons in the first shell. Lithium (Li, atomic number 3), the first element in period 2, follows helium and so has one more electron, but this electron is in a new outer shell. Neon (Ne, atomic number 10), the last element in period 2, also has two shells and has eight electrons in the outer shells, and so on. As shells are added, so the atoms of the elements down a group get larger.

The first period consists of only two elements, hydrogen and helium. Periods 2 and 3, start with lithium and sodium, respectively, and consist of eight elements each: lithium to neon, and sodium to argon. The next two periods, 4 and 5, start with potassium and rubidium and have 18 elements in each: potassium to krypton, and rubidium to xenon.

The sixth period, headed by caesium, contains 32 elements: caesium to radon. Notice that it is condensed into 18 columns by leaving out the 14 elements that form the LANTHANIDE SERIES.

The seventh period (period 7) similarly contains 32 elements shortened into six columns by taking out the 14 elements of the ACTINIDE SERIES.

Elements in the same group (column) tend to have similar chemical properties. Some groups have been given distinctive names. The elements of Group 1, for example, are called ALKALI METALS because the word alkali is derived from the Arabic for plant ash; and both sodium and potassium compounds are present in plant ash. Their hydroxides are very soluble (bases dissolve in water to become alkalis).

The elements in Group 2 are called the ALKALINE EARTH METALS. They can all form two bonds and therefore have a VALENCY of 2.

Copper, silver, and gold are called COINAGE METALS because of their use in coins. The halogens, which include chlorine, derive their name from the Greek for salt-formers, and so on.

Metals, non-metals, and metalloids

As well as fitting into groups, periods and blocks, elements can also be categorised as METALS, NON-METALS, and METALLOIDS (also called semiconductors and semi-metals).

Most metals, such as copper, are good conductors of electricity and heat. Any element that does not conduct electricity, such as chlorine, is a non-metal. Metalloids, or semiconductors, are poor conductors of electricity, but their conductivities increase when they are heated (the opposite to metals). Silicon is an important member of this class.

About three-quarters of all elements are metals, and (with the exception of hydrogen) occupy the left-hand side of the Periodic Table. The metalloids form a narrow band near the right-hand side, and the non-metals group falls mainly to the far right. Metallic character increases down a group so, for example, carbon at the top of Group 4, shows many typical non-metallic properties (for instance, it forms an acidic oxide, CO_2); lead, at the bottom of the group, is a typical metal and forms a large number of SALTS. Thus metallic properties generally increase towards the bottom left of the table, and non-metallic properties increase toward the upper right portion.

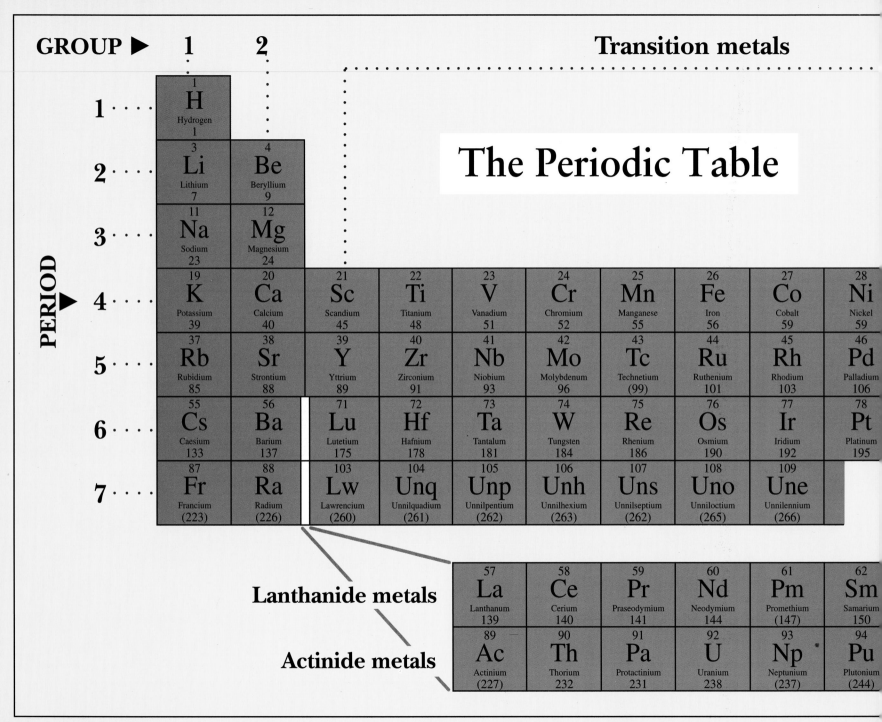

The Periodic Table

3	4	5	6	7	8
					2 **He** Helium 4
5 **B** Boron 11	6 **C** Carbon 12	7 **N** Nitrogen 14	8 **O** Oxygen 16	9 **F** Fluorine 19	10 **Ne** Neon 20
13 **Al** Aluminium 27	14 **Si** Silicon 28	15 **P** Phosphorus 31	16 **S** Sulphur 32	17 **Cl** Chlorine 35	18 **Ar** Argon 40
31 **Ga** Gallium 70	32 **Ge** Germanium 73	33 **As** Arsenic 75	34 **Se** Selenium 79	35 **Br** Bromine 80	36 **Kr** Krypton 84
49 **In** Indium 115	50 **Sn** Tin 119	51 **Sb** Antimony 122	52 **Te** Tellurium 128	53 **I** Iodine 127	54 **Xe** Xenon 131
81 **Tl** Thallium 204	82 **Pb** Lead 207	83 **Bi** Bismuth 209	84 **Po** Polonium (209)	85 **At** Astatine (210)	86 **Rn** Radon (222)

Columns to the left (groups 1 and 2 area shown):

29 **Cu** Copper 64	30 **Zn** Zinc 65	
47 **Ag** Silver 108	48 **Cd** Cadmium 112	
79 **Au** Gold 197	80 **Hg** Mercury 201	

KEY

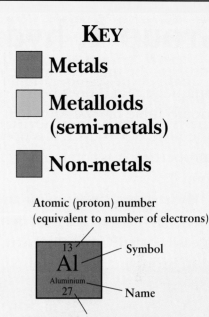

■ **Metals**

■ **Metalloids (semi-metals)**

■ **Non-metals**

Atomic (proton) number (equivalent to number of electrons) — Symbol — Name

13 **Al** Aluminium 27

Approximate relative atomic mass (approximate atomic weight). Those in brackets are radioactive.

RELATIVE ATOMIC MASS

Chemists used to compare the mass of an atom of an element with that of hydrogen. Hydrogen has one proton and one electron and is the lightest of atoms, so the mass of other elements could be given relative to hydrogen: mass of one atom of element ÷ mass of one atom of hydrogen. Nowadays, for accuracy, they compare the mass with that of carbon: mass of one atom of element ÷ mass of $\frac{1}{12}$ atom of carbon; and the $^{12}_{6}C$ ISOTOPE is used. The relative atomic mass of iodine, for example, is 127. This means that an atom of iodine is 127 times as heavy as one atom of hydrogen.

The figures used in this book are approximate and so are correctly referred to as the approximate relative atomic mass (the old term used was atomic weight). They are shown underneath the name of each element in the Periodic Table.

63 **Eu** Europium 152	64 **Gd** Gadolinium 157	65 **Tb** Terbium 159	66 **Dy** Dysprosium 163	67 **Ho** Holmium 165	68 **Er** Erbium 167	69 **Tm** Thulium 169	70 **Yb** Ytterbium 173
95 **Am** Americium (243)	96 **Cm** Curium (247)	97 **Bk** Berkelium (247)	98 **Cf** Californium (251)	99 **Es** Einsteinium (252)	100 **Fm** Fermium (257)	101 **Md** Mendelevium (258)	102 **No** Nobelium (259)

Group 1 metals, the alkali metals

The elements below hydrogen in Group 1 are called the Group 1 metals, or alkali metals. They are lithium, sodium, potassium, rubidium, caesium and francium. All are soft, silvery-coloured metals and tarnish quickly on exposure to air.

Group 1 elements have one electron in their outer shell. They are the most reactive of all the metals because the single electron in the outer shell is outside a filled shell which shields it from the nucleus – it is not strongly tied to the atom and is easily lost through reaction.

Those elements at the bottom of the alkali metal group are the most reactive: francium (which is radioactive), caesium and rubidium, burn spontaneously in air. Sodium and potassium burn when heated gently. Lithium, the metal nearest the top of the group, is the most stable, and reacts least violently with air or water.

Although all Group 1 metals occur as solids at room temperature, they are so reactive that they must be stored under some inert liquid such as oil or cyclohexane to keep them from reacting with air (① & ②).

Every alkali metal reacts with cold water, releasing hydrogen gas and producing a solution of the hydroxide of the metal that is alkaline – hence the name alkali metals. In other words they form strong bases, which produce solutions with a pH greater than 7. An example is sodium hydroxide,

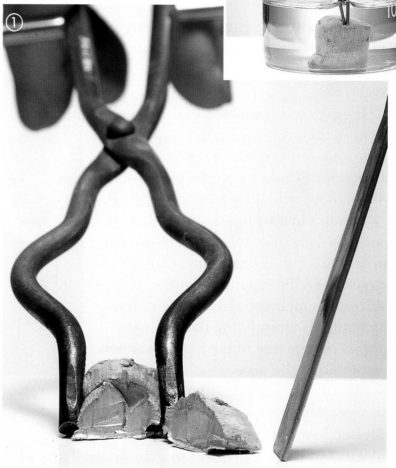

②

(*Below*) Sodium is soft, and this pellet of sodium is being carefully cut open using a spatula. The silvery-coloured sodium tarnishes quickly, reacting with oxygen in the air to produce a dull oxide coating. The metal may even ignite and catch alight. For this reason sodium is stored in a suitably inert liquid such as cyclohexane (*right*).

①

commonly known as caustic soda. These reactions always result in heat being produced – they are EXOTHERMIC.

The elements in Group 1 are so reactive that they are not found uncombined in nature and form some of the most stable of metal compounds, which are difficult to break up into their component elements. Stability of the compounds increases as the reactivity of the element increases, and the atoms become larger, down the group. As a result:

(a) crystals of sodium hydroxide are stable to heat and will melt, rather than break down, if heated on a crucible lid.

(b) washing soda crystals (hydrated sodium carbonate) will lose their water of crystallisation if heated in a tube, but the anhydrous sodium carbonate is then stable and will melt.

(c) the NITRATES must be heated to increasingly high temperatures down the group to cause decomposition, and the typical products are the metal nitrite and oxygen (only lithium nitrate gives off nitrogen dioxide) (see Group 2 elements on page 20). The metal nitrite then simply remains molten and does not decompose further.

These, and other properties, are shown in demonstrations on the next four pages.

It is the high reactivity of alkali metals that explains why they cannot be extracted by reacting their ores with other chemicals such as reducing agents. Instead, they are all obtained by passing an electric current (ELECTROLYSIS) through their molten salts. Sodium and potassium, for example, are extracted by electrolysis of molten sea salt.

GROUP 1 ELEMENTS, THE ALKALI METALS

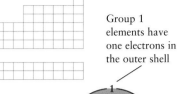

Relative size of a hydrogen atom

Group 1 elements have one electrons in the outer shell

Lithium, from the Greek for stone, 'lithos'; chemical symbol Li; Group 1, period 2; alkali metal; soft, silvery solid; atomic number 3; approximate relative atomic mass 7.

Sodium, from the English 'soda' and the Latin 'natrium'; chemical symbol Na; Group 1, period 3; alkali metal; soft, silvery solid; atomic number 11; approximate relative atomic mass 23.

Potassium, from the English 'potash', and the Latin 'kalium' and Arabic 'qali' for alkali; chemical symbol K; Group 1, period 4; alkali metal; soft, silvery solid; atomic number 19; approximate relative atomic mass 39.

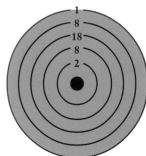

Rubidium, from the Latin for deep red, 'rubidus'; chemical symbol Rb; Group 1, period 5; alkali metal; soft, silvery solid; atomic number 37; approximate relative atomic mass 85.

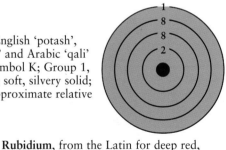

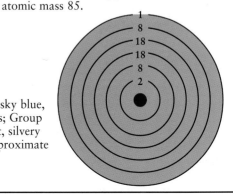

Caesium, from the Latin for sky blue, 'caesius'; chemical symbol Cs; Group 1, period 6; alkali metal; soft, silvery solid; atomic number 55; approximate relative atomic mass 133.

Demonstration 1: sodium reacts with water to form an alkaline solution of the metal hydroxide

Sodium metal is very reactive and so this demonstration is conducted in a fume chamber.

A small beaker is half filled with distilled water. An indicator is added to show the change in acidity (pH) of the solution. Phenolphthalein is used here and is colourless unless the solution becomes alkaline, in which case it turns bright pink.

A small piece of sodium is dropped on to the water and immediately begins to react with the water, fizzing as gas is produced (③). The pellet skims rapidly back and forth across the water surface leaving a trail of alkaline solution in the water (④). The heat released causes the metal to form a rolling molten ball that gets smaller and smaller and may even leap out of the container.

The reaction between water and sodium metal produces sodium hydroxide and hydrogen gas (the fizz). Sodium hydroxide solution is strongly alkaline, which is why the phenolphthalein indicator turns pink.

EQUATION: Reaction of sodium metal and water
Sodium + water ➭ sodium hydroxide + hydrogen
$2Na(s) + 2H_2O(l)$ ➭ $2NaOH(aq) + H_2(g)$
Heat given out

③

Beaker of water with phenolphthalein indicator added

Sodium pellet

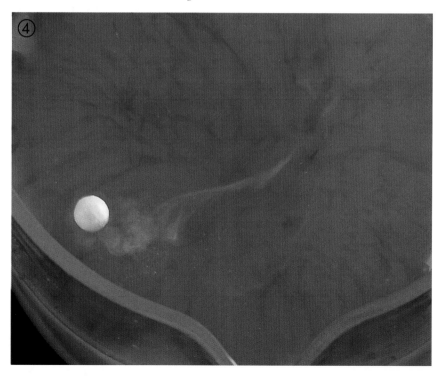
④

16

Demonstration 2: potassium reacts more vigorously with water than sodium does

Potassium metal looks very similar to sodium, but is even more reactive, and so this demonstration is conducted in a fume chamber.

When a very small pellet of potassium is added to water and phenolphthalein indicator in a beaker, it reacts violently (⑤).

Sufficient heat is produced from the reaction for the potassium to ignite the hydrogen and make it burn with a characteristic lilac flame (⑥). Combined with the rapid production of hydrogen gas, the pellet can be propelled readily from the water surface and so a deeper beaker is used.

The solution produced is potassium hydroxide (the metal hydroxide), which is very strongly alkaline, and the indicator in the solution is dark pink.

EQUATION: Reaction of potassium metal and water
Potassium + water ⇨ potassium hydroxide + hydrogen
$2K(s) + 2H_2O(l) ⇨ 2KOH(aq) + H_2(g)$
Heat given out

Demonstration 3: nitrites of Group 1 metals are stable compounds

White potassium nitrate powder is heated in a test tube using a Bunsen flame (⑦).

At high temperatures, the potassium nitrate melts to a greenish-yellow liquid (potassium nitrite). The presence of oxygen is revealed by the rekindling of a smouldering splint (⑧).

After the oxygen has been driven off, potassium nitrite is not decomposed further by heating, and a glowing splint will not rekindle. When the heat is removed, it eventually cools to a white solid (⑨).

Demonstration 4: carbonates of Group 1 metals are stable compounds

Some crystals of the hydrated salt sodium carbonate decahydrate (washing soda), are heated in a test tube (⑩). The WATER OF CRYSTALLISATION is driven off as steam, but no further change takes place and the material cools to a white powder (⑪). (As an alternative to heating, leaving the crystals in air will cause them to EFFLORESCE and turn into a white powder.)

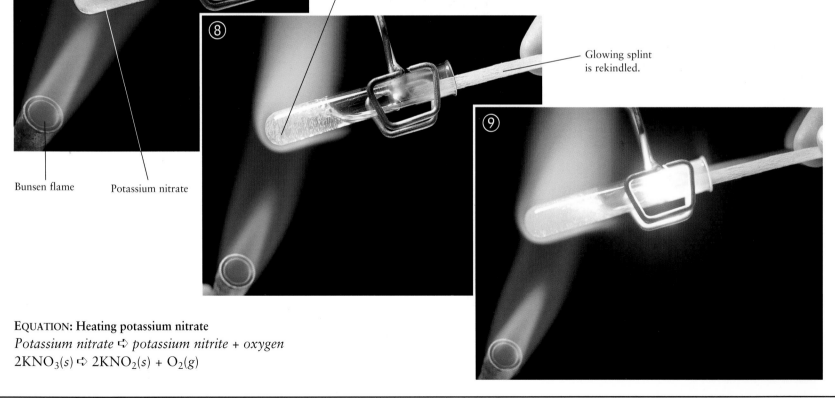

Potassium nitrite

Glowing splint is rekindled.

Bunsen flame   Potassium nitrate

EQUATION: Heating potassium nitrate

Potassium nitrate ⇨ potassium nitrite + oxygen

$2KNO_3(s) ⇨ 2KNO_2(s) + O_2(g)$

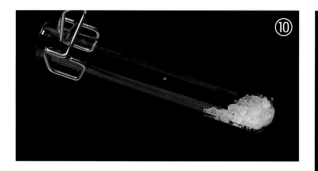

EQUATION: Heating hydrated sodium carbonate
Sodium carbonate decahydrate ⇨ *sodium carbonate + water (steam)*
$Na_2CO_3 \bullet 10H_2O(s) \Rightarrow Na_2CO_3(s) + 10H_2O(g)$

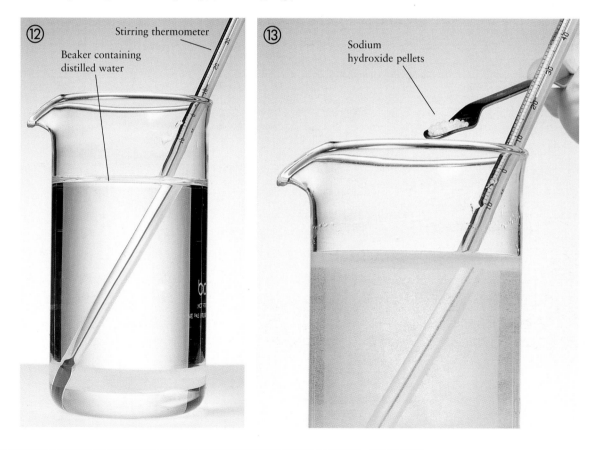

Stirring thermometer

Beaker containing
distilled water

Sodium
hydroxide pellets

Demonstration 5: almost all compounds of Group 1 metals are soluble in water

Most Group 1 compounds dissolve very readily in water, some reacting to liberate heat and form a strongly alkaline solution.

If sodium hydroxide crystals are added to some distilled water at room temperature (⑫) and stirred with a stirring thermometer, the temperature of the solution rises – in this case by 10°C, as can be seen on the thermometer (⑬).

Group 2 elements, the alkaline earth metals

The elements in Group 2 are all metals and are known as the alkaline earths. They are the metals beryllium, magnesium, calcium, strontium, barium and radium. All Group 2 elements except beryllium are soft, white metals that are solid at room temperature and tarnish in air.

Group 2 elements have two electrons in their outer shell. Because they have to lose two electrons to make a chemical reaction, they are not quite as reactive as Group 1 elements. They do not, for example, ignite spontaneously. As with the Group 1 elements, reactivity increases down the group. Barium is kept under oil; magnesium is not. The compounds formed by those metals higher up the group are more easily broken down into their component elements or compounds. Beryllium is unusual in this group because its properties are closer to aluminium in Group 3 (see page 36). Radium is radioactive.

The alkaline earths all burn in air, often with characteristic colours (① & ②). Calcium, for example, produces a brick-red flame.

Each element in Group 2, except beryllium, reacts with water to release hydrogen and form an alkaline solution of the metal hydroxide. Calcium, for example, reacts with water to produce hydrogen and calcium hydroxide (also known as limewater). Calcium reacts steadily with water at room temperature, whereas magnesium only reacts, at a significant rate, with steam.

At ordinary temperatures, calcium and metals below it in Group 2 react readily with oxygen in air to form oxides (③). The oxides of Group 2 metals react with water to form hydroxides that are strongly alkaline (the term 'alkaline earths' refers to the alkaline oxides of Group 2 metals). A considerable amount of energy is released from this reaction as heat, as shown by the slaking of quicklime (turning the oxide into the hydroxide by adding water). Conversely, the hydroxides can only be converted to oxides by extreme heating; that is, they are very ENDOTHERMIC reactions.

The NITRATES of Group 2 elements decompose to give an oxide, brown nitrogen dioxide gas, and oxygen. This is in contrast with most of the nitrates of Group 1 elements that give only an oxide and oxygen.

The carbonates further down the group are harder to decompose (it requires a furnace to decompose calcium carbonate and produce calcium oxide, for example, whereas magnesium carbonate can be decomposed by a Bunsen flame).

A further trend down Group 2 is the decreasing solubility of the SULPHATES. Thus $MgSO_4$ (Epsom salts) is very soluble in water, whereas $BaSO_4$ is insoluble even in hot water, and is readily formed as a precipitate (this makes the basis of the test for sulphates).

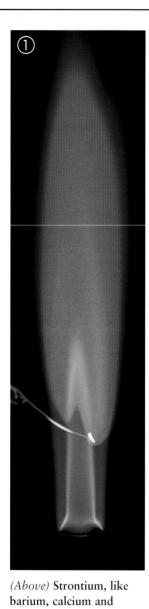

①

②

③

(Below) Calcium rapidly reacts with oxygen in the air to form a protective (dull) oxide coating that tends to prevent any further reaction. It only looks silvery when freshly cut.

Magnesium ribbon cleaned with emery paper

Magnesium oxide

Magnesium ribbon with dull oxide coating

(Above) **Strontium**, like barium, calcium and magnesium, is an element in Group 2. When strontium or its compounds are burnt, they produce a characteristic crimson-coloured flame.

GROUP 2 ELEMENTS, THE ALKALINE EARTH METALS

Relative size of a hydrogen atom

Group 2 elements have two electrons in the outer shell

Beryllium, named after the mineral beryl; chemical symbol Be; Group 2, period 2; alkaline earth metal; soft, grey solid; atomic number 4; approximate relative atomic mass 9.

Magnesium, named after a region in Greece called Magnesia; chemical symbol Mg; Group 2, period 3; alkaline earth metal; soft, silvery solid; atomic number 12; approximate relative atomic mass 24.

Calcium, from the Latin for lime, 'calx'; Group 2, period 4; chemical symbol Ca; alkaline earth metal; soft, silvery solid; atomic number 20; approximate relative atomic mass 40.

Strontium, named after Strontian, a place in Scotland; chemical symbol Sr; Group 2, period 5; alkaline earth metal; soft, silvery solid; atomic number 38; approximate relative atomic mass 88.

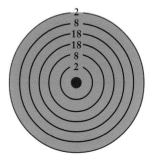

Barium, from the Greek for heavy, 'barys'; chemical symbol Ba; Group 2, period 6; alkaline earth metal; soft, silver–yellow solid; atomic number 56; approximate relative atomic mass 137.

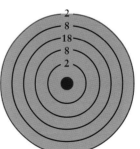

Demonstration 1: the reaction of calcium with water

For this demonstration, a gas jar is filled with water and upturned in a pneumatic trough, which is also filled with water.

Some small pellets of calcium (④) are dropped into the water and sink to the bottom. The mouth of the gas jar is immediately placed over the pellet.

Soon, the calcium pellets react with the water as is typical of Group 2 metals, although this reaction is much less vigorous than that for potassium which is in the same period of Group 1 (see page 17). Bubbles of hydrogen gas are produced and surround each pellet. These bubbles lift the pellets to the surface of the water at the top of the gas jar (⑤). The bubbles then burst, allowing the pellets to fall to the bottom again, whilst hydrogen accumulates at the top of the gas jar. As a result, the pellets are continually moving up and down in the gas jar.

However, the reaction produces colourless calcium hydroxide as well as hydrogen. The calcium hydroxide, also called limewater, accumulates until the solution becomes saturated. The excess calcium hydroxide now forms a fine, white PRECIPITATE, which remains in suspension and makes the solution cloudy in appearance. The calcium hydroxide solution is an alkali that can be tested if an indicator is added.

The gas collected in the gas jar can be tested, once the solution is removed. If a lighted splint is introduced into the gas jar, the hydrogen ignites with a loud high-pitched popping sound.

EQUATION: Calcium in water
Calcium + water ⇨ hydrogen gas + calcium hydroxide
$Ca(s) + 2H_2O(l) ⇨ H_2(g) + Ca(OH)_2(aq)$
Heat given out

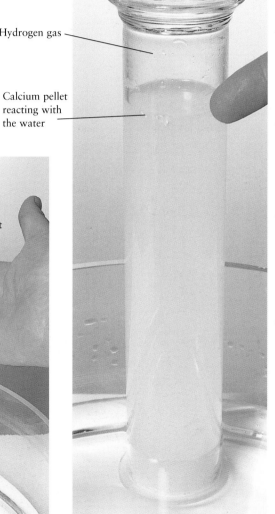

⑤

Hydrogen gas

Calcium pellet reacting with the water

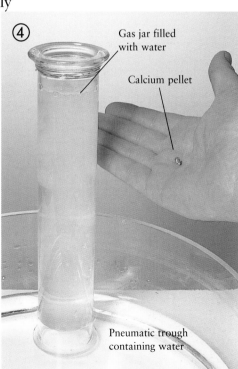

④

Gas jar filled with water

Calcium pellet

Pneumatic trough containing water

Demonstration 2: the reaction of magnesium and steam

Magnesium is higher up Group 2 than calcium. It is less reactive and will only react slowly with cold water. Heated magnesium will, however, react violently with hot water or steam. As a result, this demonstration is done in a fume chamber.

A small quantity of mineral (and therefore heat-resistant) wool is soaked in water and placed in the far end of a boiling tube. The tube is clamped horizontally, and a spatula is then used to spread some magnesium granules along the length of the tube.

The end of the tube is fitted with a stopper and a delivery tube so that the gas coming from the reaction can be collected and tested.

The heating is done with a Bunsen flame. The flame is played on the glass below the granules until they are very hot (⑥).

Gradually, the heat reaches the water at the end of the tube, turning the water into steam. As the steam fills the boiling tube, it reacts with the granules, generating a spectacular reaction that causes the granules to combust with an intense white glow (⑦).

The reaction is now self-sustaining and the Bunsen flame is withdrawn. The white light continues to be produced as the remaining steam and magnesium react. When the reaction is complete, the white material in the tube is an ash of magnesium oxide. The gas produced from the reaction can be collected in the gas jar by downward displacement over water and is then tested with a flame. A popping sound as the flame is put into the gas jar shows the gas to be hydrogen.

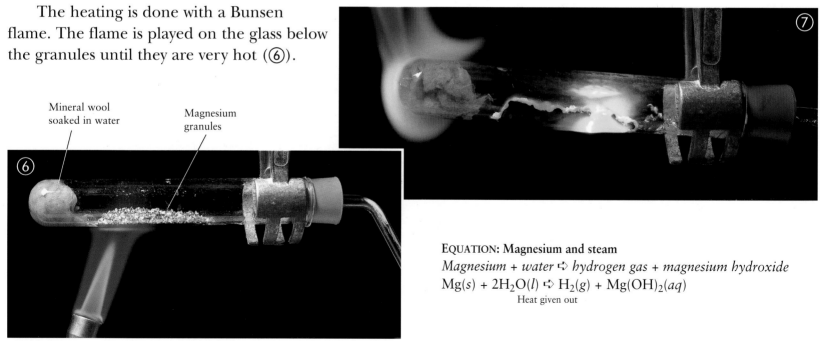

Mineral wool soaked in water

Magnesium granules

⑥

⑦

EQUATION: Magnesium and steam

Magnesium + water ⇨ hydrogen gas + magnesium hydroxide

$Mg(s) + 2H_2O(l) \Rightarrow H_2(g) + Mg(OH)_2(aq)$

Heat given out

Demonstration 3: decomposing calcium carbonate

Compounds of Group 2 metals are very stable. Calcium carbonate (limestone), for example, only DECOMPOSES at furnace temperatures.

In this laboratory demonstration, a block of limestone is placed in a small iron cylinder kiln (⑧) and is heated using several Bunsen flames (⑨) until it becomes yellow-hot (⑩). Only at this high temperature does the limestone decompose to form a white solid, calcium oxide, and give off carbon dioxide gas.

Calcium oxide, commonly known as quicklime, is produced industrially by roasting limestone in huge rotating kilns. Quicklime is used for cement and whitewash.

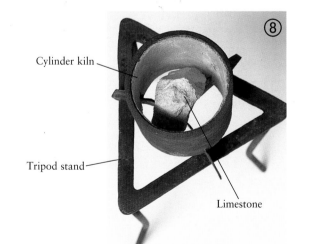

⑧

Cylinder kiln

Tripod stand

Limestone

EQUATION: Calcium carbonate decomposes
Calcium carbonate ⇨ calcium oxide + carbon dioxide
$CaCO_3(s) ⇨ CaO(s) + CO_2(g)$

⑨

Conical cover keeps heat inside the kiln

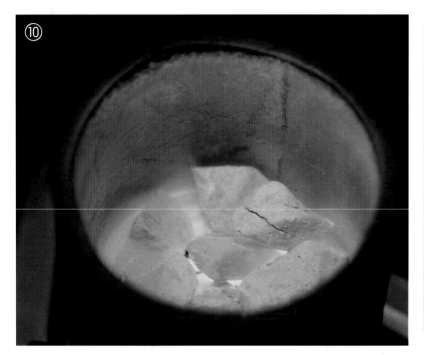

Demonstration 4: reaction of calcium oxide with water

Calcium hydroxide can be decomposed, but only with more energy than can easily be obtained in a laboratory furnace. So, this demonstration reveals the amount of heat required by showing the energy given out by the reverse process, namely the reaction of the oxide with water.

Some small blocks of calcium oxide are placed on a watch glass. Some drops of water are added to a few of the blocks using a pipette (⑪), leaving some blocks untouched to act as a visual control.

Water instantly reacts with the calcium oxide. The reaction is very EXOTHERMIC and the reacting blocks of calcium oxide become extremely hot, swelling and driving some of the water off as steam (⑫).

The blocks of reacting calcium oxide then expand and begin to crack. Eventually they collapse to a dry powder, calcium hydroxide. The powder is very basic, making an alkaline solution in water.

EQUATION: The formation of calcium hydroxide
Calcium oxide + water ⇨ calcium hydroxide
$CaO(s) + H_2O(l) \Rightarrow Ca(OH)_2(aq)$
Heat given out

Demonstration 5: Group 2 metals are more reactive than the transition metals and those in Group 3 or higher

Although Group 2 metals are less reactive than those in Group 1, they are much more reactive than most other metals. This is easily shown by the way that magnesium displaces the metals from many soluble compounds of higher groups.

The reactivity of metals can be represented in a table showing a REACTIVITY SERIES. The one shown below is for commonly available laboratory metals and their salts.

(Right) **The relative position of each metal in the reactivity series allows you to predict which metal will displace the other from solution. If one metal is above the other in the series, it will displace the lower reactivity metal from a solution.**

Those metals above hydrogen in the series will reduce hydrogen ions in an acid solution to liberate hydrogen gas. Those below hydrogen in the table will not.

THE METAL REACTIVITY SERIES		
Element	Reactivity	Reducing or oxidising power
Potassium Sodium Calcium Magnesium Aluminium Manganese Chromium Zinc Iron Cadmium Tin Lead *Hydrogen* Copper Mercury Silver Gold Platinum	*Increasing reactivity* ↑	*Most strongly reducing or least strongly oxidising* ↕ *Least strongly reducing or most strongly oxidising*

Magnesium displaces iron

When a piece of magnesium ribbon is placed in a bottle containing some almost colourless iron(II) sulphate solution (⑬), there is a vigorous reaction (⑭).

EQUATION TO SHOW ION MOVEMENTS
$$Mg(s) + Fe^{2+}(aq) \Rightarrow Mg^{2+}(aq) + Fe(s)$$

The iron is displaced from the solution and is precipitated on the surface of the magnesium and hydrogen gas is evolved. Magnesium metal is converted into ions and passes into solution.

Magnesium ribbon

⑬   ⑭

The turbulence resulting from the evolution of hydrogen dislodges the small particles of iron precipitated around the magnesium ribbon and they fall away.

Magnesium displaces lead

A magnesium strip is placed in a bottle containing lead nitrate solution (⑮). The magnesium strip changes rapidly (⑯).

EQUATION TO SHOW ION MOVEMENTS
$$Mg(s) + Pb^{2+}(aq) \Rightarrow Mg^{2+}(aq) + Pb(s)$$

The magnesium metal displaces lead from the lead nitrate solution. Lead is rapidly precipitated on the surface of the magnesium ribbon. The particle size increases to a point where reflection from the surface of the lead crystals is apparent as a shiny sheen. This reaction is more rapid than that between magnesium and iron because magnesium and lead are further apart in the reactivity series.

Magnesium displaces silver

When a piece of magnesium ribbon is placed in a bottle of silver nitrate solution (⑰), the magnesium changes very rapidly indeed (⑱).

EQUATION TO SHOW ION MOVEMENTS
$$Mg(s) + 2Ag^{+}(aq) \Rightarrow Mg^{2+}(aq) + 2Ag(s)$$

The magnesium metal displaces silver from the silver solution. Silver is precipitated very rapidly on the surface of the magnesium ribbon. The particle size increases to a point where reflection from the surface of the silver crystals is apparent as a metallic lustre.

This reaction is even more rapid than that between magnesium and lead because magnesium and silver are even further apart in the reactivity series.

⑮  ⑯

The precipitate will not stick to the magnesium and falls to the bottom of the bottle.

⑰ ⑱

The transition metals

The transition metals lie between Groups 2 and 3 and make up the central block of the Periodic Table. The transition metals are very widely used. Iron is used for construction, copper for electrical cables, titanium for aerospace and the precious metals, platinum, silver and gold, are prized for their rarity.

Each row (period) in this block is known as a transition series. As one moves from left to right along a series, each additional electron is not added to the outermost shell; instead, the electron joins the previous, or penultimate, shell (see the shell diagrams for titanium and vanadium in period 4, for example). This characteristic makes the transition elements different from the other elements in the Periodic Table and is responsible for many of their characteristics.

The members of the transition metals are (those which are more commonly found are shown in bold): scandium, yttrium, lutetium, lawrencium, **titanium**, **zirconium**, hafnium, unnilquadrium, **vanadium**, niobium, **tantalum**, unnilpentium, **chromium**, **molybdenum**, **tungsten**, unnilhexium, **manganese**, technetium, rhenium, unniseptium, **iron**, ruthenium, osmium, unniloctium, **cobalt**, rhodium, iridium, unnilennium, **nickel**, palladium, **platinum**, **copper**, **silver**, **gold**, **zinc**, **cadmium**, and **mercury**.

In addition, there are groups of very rare elements that make up part of the transition metals. These elements are part of the lanthanide series and actinide series of metals and are shown at the foot of the Periodic Table.

Transition metals have an incomplete penultimate and outside shell of electrons. One or two electrons are found in the outer shell.

THE TRANSITION METALS

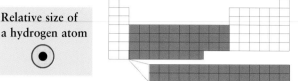

Relative size of a hydrogen atom

Titanium, named after the Titans who were Greek mythological figures; chemical symbol Ti; transition metal, period 4; light, strong, silvery solid; atomic number 22; approximate relative atomic mass 48.

Zirconium, from the Arabic for gold colour, 'zargun'; chemical symbol Zr; transition metal, period 5; grey–white solid; atomic number 40; approximate relative atomic mass 91.

Vanadium, named after the mythical Scandinavian goddess of colour, Vanadis; chemical symbol Va; transition metal, period 4; soft, silver–white solid; atomic number 23; approximate relative atomic mass 51.

Tantalum, named after Tantalos, Greek mythological figure; chemical symbol Ta; transition metal, period 6; steel–grey colour; atomic number 73; approximate relative atomic mass 181.

Chromium, from the Greek for colour, 'chroma'; chemical symbol Cr; transition metal, period 4; hard, corrosion resistant, silvery solid; atomic number 24; approximate relative atomic mass 52.

Molybdenum, from the Greek for lead, 'molybdos'; chemical symbol Mo; transition metal, period 5; hard, silvery solid; atomic number 42; approximate relative atomic mass 96.

Tungsten, from the Swedish for heavy stone, 'tung sten'; chemical symbol W; transition metal, period 6; hard, steel–grey solid; atomic number 74; approximate relative atomic mass 184.

Manganese, from the Greek or Latin for magnet, 'magnes'; chemical symbol Mn; transition metal, period 4; hard, grey–white solid; atomic number 25; approximate relative atomic mass 55.

Iron, from the Anglo-Saxon 'iron' and the Latin 'ferrum'; chemical symbol Fe; transition metal, period 4; quite hard, grey solid; atomic number 26; approximate relative atomic mass 56.

Cobalt, from the Greek for goblin, 'kobalos' and the German evil spirit, 'Kobald'; chemical symbol Co; transition metal, period 4; hard, steel–grey solid; atomic number 27; approximate relative atomic mass 59.

Nickel, from the German for Satan, The Devil, 'Nickel'; chemical symbol Ni; transition metal, period 4; hard, silver–white solid; atomic number 28; approximate relative atomic mass 59.

Platinum, from the Spanish for silver, 'plata'; chemical symbol Pt; transition metal, period 6; soft, silvery solid; atomic number 78; approximate relative atomic mass 195.

Copper, from the Latin for Cyprus, 'cuprum'; chemical symbol Cu; transition metal, period 4; quite soft, orange–red solid; atomic number 29; approximate relative atomic mass 64.

The lanthanide metals are: lanthanium, cerium, praseodymium, neodymium, promethium, samarium, europium, gadolinium, terbium, dysprosium, holmium, erbium, thulium, and ytterbium.

The actinide metals are: actinium, thorium, protactinium, **uranium**, neptunium, **plutonium**, americium, curium, berkelium, californium, einsteinium, fermium, mendelevium and nobelium.

Properties

The transition elements are all metals and have the following general properties:

- They have one or two electrons in their outer shells.
- They are all hard and strong, with high densities, high melting and boiling points (for example, platinum).
- They form a number of OXIDATION STATES (for example, iron(II) and iron(III)).
- They tend to form coloured compounds (for example, iron(II) compounds are often green and iron(III) compounds are often orange–brown).
- Many are CATALYSTS (for example, vanadium and manganese).
- Many are good conductors of heat and electricity (for example, silver and copper).
- Many can be bent easily (they are beaten easily into sheets or drawn into wires, for example, iron).
- They all form basic oxides (but some can also be amphoteric (for example, zinc) and even acidic where higher oxidation states exist (for example, manganese(VII) oxide)).
- Most of them quickly develop a protective oxide coating when exposed to air and most are fairly unreactive (for example, gold).
- When they react, they tend to lose electrons, forming positive ions, CATIONS (for example, Fe^{2+} and Mn^{2+}).

THE TRANSITION METALS

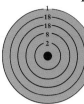

Silver, from the Anglo-Saxon 'seolfor' and the Latin 'argentum'; chemical symbol Ag; transition metal, period 5; soft, silver-coloured solid; atomic number 47; approximate relative atomic mass 108.

Gold, from the Anglo-Saxon 'gold' and the Latin 'aurum'; chemical symbol Au; transition metal, period 6; soft, yellow solid; atomic number 79; approximate relative atomic mass 197.

Zinc, from the Anglo-Saxon 'zinc'; chemical symbol Zn; transition metal, period 4; hard, blue–white solid; atomic number 30; approximate relative atomic mass 65.

Cadmium, named after the Greek hero Cadmus; chemical symbol Cd; transition metal, period 5; hard, blue–white solid; atomic number 48; approximate relative atomic mass 112.

Mercury, named after the planet Mercury and the Latin for liquid silver or quicksilver, 'hydrargyrum'; chemical symbol Hg; transition metal, period 6; silvery <u>liquid</u>; atomic number 80; approximate relative atomic mass 201.

Uranium, named after the planet Uranus; chemical symbol U; actinide metal, period 7, radioactive; soft, silvery solid; atomic number 92; approximate relative atomic mass 238.

Plutonium, named after the planet Pluto; chemical symbol Pu; actinide metal, period 7, radioactive; silvery solid; atomic number 94; approximate relative atomic mass (244).

Demonstration 1: small-scale reduction of iron by aluminium

The transition metals have high melting points. Iron, one of the most widely used transition metals, has a melting point of about 1535°C. The standard industrial process is to use a blast furnace to REDUCE it from its oxide to the pure metal. A laboratory furnace cannot reach these temperatures. This small-scale demonstration achieves the required temperature and uses a Group 3 metal, aluminium, which is above iron in the reactivity series (see page 26), as a reducing agent.

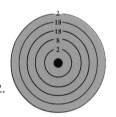

① Magnesium ribbon

Barium peroxide

A mixture of aluminium and iron oxide in a glass boiling tube

Sand in an old tin can catches the molten mixture.

②

All of the apparatus used in this demonstration will be destroyed. Therefore, the apparatus used consists of an old tin can which has been filled with sand. An old boiling tube is partly buried in the sand. The boiling tube contains a mixture of iron(III) oxide and aluminium powder (①). A strip of magnesium ribbon acts as a fuse. The lower end of the ribbon sits on a hollow in the iron/aluminium powder, which has been filled with barium peroxide.

When the magnesium ribbon is ignited, it will burn down into the barium peroxide, which is an oxidiser (②). The reaction will make the magnesium glow much more brightly (③) as it rises to a temperature high enough to cause a reaction between the aluminium and iron in which the iron oxide is reduced and the aluminium oxidised to aluminium oxide. The aluminium oxide is a lightweight, fine powder, which is easily carried aloft by the rising currents of hot air as a white smoke (④).

The molten iron and glass mixture is caught in the sand (⑤ & ⑥, see page 32). Once it has cooled (⑦ & ⑧, see page 33), the glass can be knocked away to reveal the iron (⑨).

Remarks

Although this demonstration is on a small scale, because of the extremely high temperatures reached during the reaction (about 2000°C), this demonstration cannot be done safely in a laboratory and was performed in the open air under close supervision, with the supervisor and photographer wearing appropriate safety equipment, and with no spectators nearby.

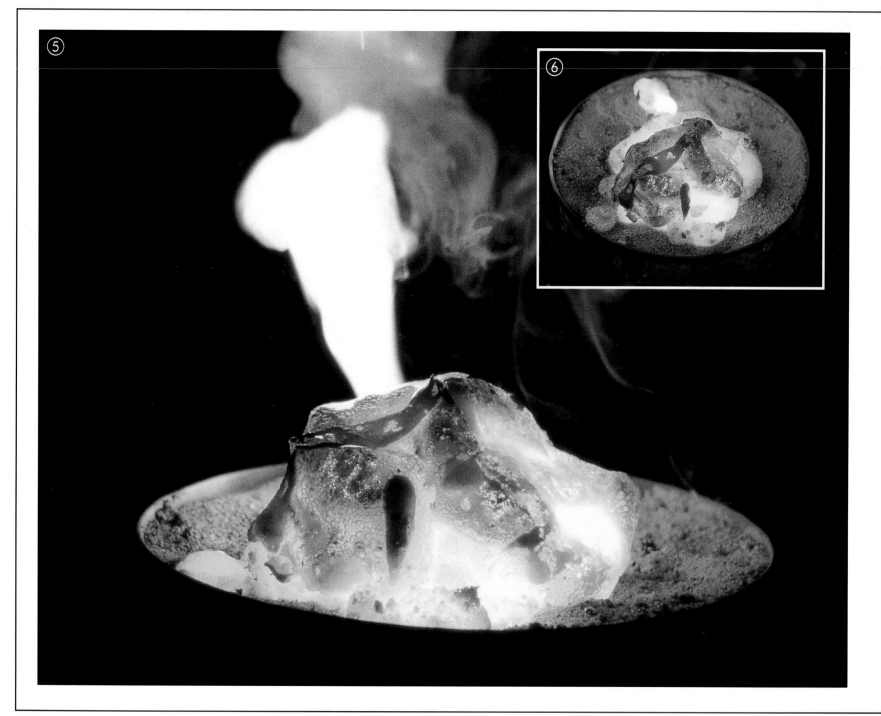

⑤

⑥

32

(7)

(Below) Like many of the transition metals, iron is used widely. Each transition metal has different uses, depending on its physical and chemical characteristics, which are, in turn, a reflection of its atomic structure.

The metal's use depends on its reactivity with other elements and compounds, its melting point, its hardness, strength, as well as its ability to conduct electricity and heat.

Iron is hard and durable, but can be beaten into sheets or drawn out into wires. Importantly, the ore from which it is extracted is abundant in the Earth's crust.

EQUATION: Reduction of iron(III) oxide to iron

Iron(III) oxide + aluminium ⇨ iron + aluminium oxide

$$Fe_2O_3(s) + 2Al(s) \rightarrow 2Fe(s) + Al_2O_3(s)$$

(8)

(9)

Refined iron

Demonstration 2: transition colours of vanadium

Transition metals can have several OXIDATION STATES, due to the electron arrangement of their atoms. Many transition metals show a number of colours as they change oxidation state. This can be illustrated by a demonstration using vanadium compounds.

Concentrated hydrochloric acid is added to ammonium vanadate in a test tube (⑩). Under these conditions, the yellow vanadate ions contain vanadium in its highest oxidation state of 5.

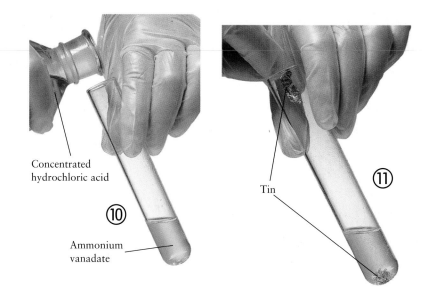

Concentrated hydrochloric acid

⑩

Ammonium vanadate

Tin

⑪

⑫

Vanadium(V), oxidation state 5, yellow

Vanadium(IV), oxidation state 4, blue

Vanadium(III), oxidation state 3, green

Vanadium(II), oxidation state 2, violet

A piece of tin is then added (⑪), which makes it effervesce with small streams of hydrogen bubbles. The tin and concentrated acid make up a reducing system that removes electrons from the vanadium ions.

As electrons are removed, so the vanadium is reduced from vanadium(V), to vanadium(IV) and vanadium(III), and finally to vanadium(II). The series of pictures, at the bottom of the opposite page, shows the colour changes associated with the vanadium ions as they change oxidation state (⑫).

Demonstration 3: transition metals as catalysts

A catalyst is a substance that speeds up a reaction but itself remains unchanged. The demonstration shown here can be quite violent, and to contain the reaction products, it is performed in the bottom of a gas jar. A compound of the transition metal, cobalt, is used as a catalyst.

If colourless sodium hydroxide is added to orange-coloured cobalt chloride, a dark blue precipitate of cobalt(II) hydroxide is formed (⑬).

This cobalt hydroxide precipitate is an excellent catalyst for the decomposition of hydrogen peroxide. So, when hydrogen peroxide is added to the gas jar (⑭), oxygen is instantly produced, and effervescence occurs, nearly filling the gas jar with froth (⑮). The reaction is complete within a few seconds.

⑬ Sodium hydroxide

⑭ Hydrogen peroxide solution

⑮

Cobalt chloride

Dark blue precipitate of cobalt(II) hydroxide will act as a catalyst.

EQUATION: Decomposition of hydrogen peroxide using cobalt(II) hydroxide
Hydrogen peroxide ⇨ water + oxygen
$H_2O_2(aq) ⇨ H_2O(l) + O_2(g)$
Catalyst of cobalt(II) hydroxide ($Co(OH)_2$)

Group 3 elements

Across Groups 3 to 8 the chemical properties of the elements change from metallic to non-metallic. The elements also become progressively more metallic in character towards the bottom of each of these groups, and more non-metallic towards the top.

The elements in Group 3 are boron, aluminium, gallium, indium and thallium and they are characterised by having three electrons in their outer shell.

Most of the elements in this group show non-metallic as well as metallic characteristics. Thus, unlike the metals of Group 1 and 2 whose oxides and hydroxides are typically basic, an AMPHOTERIC character is clear in Group 3, and the elements react with both acids and bases. For example, aluminium is attacked by alkali even more rapidly than by acid (in part, because the protective layer of oxide on aluminium is more readily removed by an alkali).

Aluminium and boron are both lightweight and have properties of toughness.

Aluminium will displace metals low in the reactivity series (see page 26) and can therefore be used as a reducing agent (see page 30). Its high reactivity means that it forms very stable compounds. Aluminium ore (bauxite) requires very high temperatures and an electrical current (electrolysis) to extract the metal. Like the other elements in Group 3, aluminium forms positive ions with a VALENCY of 3.

GROUP 3 ELEMENTS

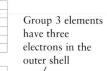

Relative size of a hydrogen atom

Group 3 elements have three electrons in the outer shell

Boron, from the Arabic for the mineral, borax, 'buraq'; chemical symbol B; Group 3, period 2; metalloid; lightweight, yellow–brown solid; atomic number 5; approximate relative atomic mass 11.

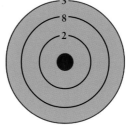

Aluminium, named after the alum salts in which the element is found; chemical symbol Al; Group 3, period 3; metal; soft, silvery-white solid; atomic number 13; approximate relative atomic mass 27.

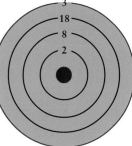

Gallium, the Latin for France, 'Gallia'; chemical symbol Ga; Group 3, period 4; metal; silvery solid; atomic number 31; approximate relative atomic mass 70.

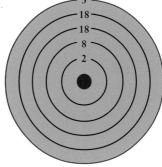

Indium, from the indigo colour it produces when burned; chemical symbol In; Group 3, period 5; metal; silvery-white solid; atomic number 49; approximate relative atomic mass 115.

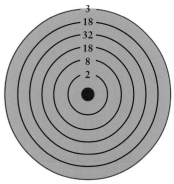

Thallium, the Greek for a green shoot of a plant, 'thallos'; chemical symbol Tl; Group 3, period 6; metal; a soft, blue–white solid; atomic number 81; approximate relative atomic mass 204.

Demonstration 1: Group 3 metals are amphoteric

Aluminium reacts with acids and alkalis. When aluminium reacts with an acid such as dilute hydrochloric acid, hydrogen gas is produced. However, the reactivity is slowed initially (and may even be prevented) by the oxide layer that forms on aluminium, making it resistant to further attack.

Aluminium is amphoteric and so will react with alkalis as well as acids. To demonstrate this, a small aluminium pie dish is placed on a watch glass and some sodium hydroxide solution, an alkali, is poured into it (①). The reaction immediately produces an effervescence. Within a few minutes, the aluminium container has been dissolved away in the region where the sodium hydroxide was in contact with it (②).

(Right)
Aluminium is about one-third of the density of iron, making it an appropriately lightweight construction material for aircraft. Aluminium is also a good conductor of heat and electricity.

① Sodium hydroxide (alkali)

Bubbles of hydrogen gas

Watch glass

Aluminium dish

②

EQUATION: Aluminium reacts with an alkali, sodium hydroxide

Aluminium + sodium hydroxide + water ⇨ sodium aluminate + hydrogen

$2Al(s) + 2NaOH(aq) + 6H_2O(l) \Rightarrow 2NaAl(OH)_4(aq) + 3H_2(g)$

Heat given out

Demonstration 2: the reaction of aluminium and bromine

Elements in Group 3 have fewer straight metallic properties than the metals in Group 1 and Group 2. However, they have not lost all of these properties. This can be demonstrated by the way aluminium still reacts with some non-metals to form salts. However, aluminium will only react with the more reactive non-metals, such as bromine as shown in this demonstration and chlorine shown on the next page. Bromine and chlorine are very poisonous, and so these demonstrations are done in a fume chamber.

For the demonstration with bromine to work at its best, a sheet of thin aluminium foil is cut up into narrow strips to increase the surface area of metal available for reaction. The strips are placed on a watch glass, and a few drops of bromine are then dripped on to the aluminium (③). The laboratory lights are then dimmed. Within a few seconds, dense smoke issues from the reactants and, shortly after this, the heat generated is sufficient to cause the reagents to glow brightly in red and orange colours (④).

When the reaction is over, the resultant compound, aluminium bromide, is left on the watch glass as a grey powder (⑤).

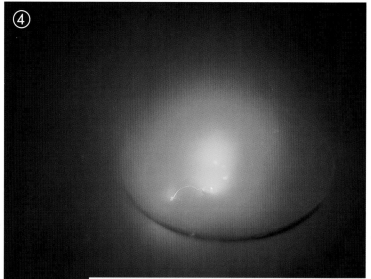

④

⑤

③
Strips of shiny aluminium

Pipette containing pure bromine liquid

EQUATION: Reaction of bromine and aluminium
Aluminium + bromine ⇨ aluminium bromide
$2Al(s) + 3Br_2(l) \Rightarrow 2AlBr_3(s)$
Heat given out

Demonstration 3: the reaction of aluminium and chlorine

Aluminium will react violently and spectacularly with chlorine, but only when it is heated strongly.

The apparatus consists of a dropper funnel and a conical flask (in which the chlorine gas is generated), a combustion tube in which the aluminium foil is placed, and a collecting vessel; in this case a side-arm conical flask connected to a suction pump that will improve the flow of chlorine through the apparatus and also remove any unreacted chlorine (⑥).

Chlorine gas is first generated by oxidising the concentrated hydrochloric acid from the dropper funnel with potassium permanganate in the conical flask. The pump allows the diffusion of chlorine along the combustion tube (made of a heat-resistant glass) so that it passes over the aluminium foil.

The aluminium foil is then heated strongly (⑧). Eventually, it begins to flare with an intense white light, while a pale yellow smoke consisting of fine particles of aluminium chloride flows into the flask (⑨). The Bunsen flame can be taken away at this stage because the reaction is exothermic and enough internal heat is generated to continue the reaction unaided.

Although not shown here, it is interesting to contrast this with the reaction between the Group 1 metal, sodium, and chlorine, which needs little or no heating and is extremely violent and exothermic.

EQUATION: Chlorine reacts with aluminium
Aluminium + chlorine ➪ aluminium(III) chloride
$$2Al(s) + 3Cl_2(g) \Rightarrow 2AlCl_3(s)$$
Heat given out

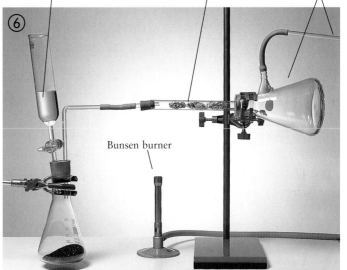

The dropper funnel allows a controlled release of hydrochloric acid on to the potassium permanganate to generate chlorine.

The aluminium foil has been pushed into a glass tube. The chlorine is passed over the aluminium foil.

A suction pump draws off waste fumes from a side-arm flask.

Bunsen burner

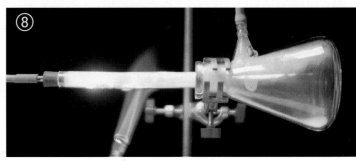

Group 4 elements

The elements in Group 4 are carbon, silicon, germanium, tin and lead, and they are characterised by having four electrons in their outer shells.

Carbon is found in 94% of the millions of compounds discovered so far, and is the essential building block of all living things. Silicon is second only to oxygen in abundance in the Earth's rocks.

As with Group 3, Group 4 elements become increasingly metallic down the group. Group 4 shows a trend from a non-metal (C), through metalloids (Si and Ge) to metals (Sn and Pb). Reactivity also increases down the group.

The carbon dioxide, produced when carbon is burnt in oxygen, dissolves in water to give carbonic acid which is a weak acid. Acidic oxides are characteristic of non-metals. Also, carbon will not react with dilute hydrochloric or sulphuric acids, suggesting that it is a non-metal. And carbon, in the form of diamond, will not conduct electricity.

Silicon and germanium show metalloid properties, being semiconductors – this characteristic is put to use in computer chips.

Tin, on the other hand, demonstrates metal properties, reacting with dilute hydrochloric acid to liberate hydrogen. Similarly, lead monoxide behaves as a base and is readily reacted with nitric acid to form a salt and water.

Lead is the most metallic member of the group. However, lead hydroxide redissolves in dilute sodium

GROUP 4 ELEMENTS

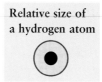
Relative size of a hydrogen atom

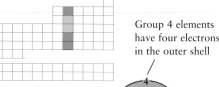

Group 4 elements have four electrons in the outer shell

Carbon, from the Latin for charcoal or coal, 'carbo'; chemical symbol C; Group 4, period 2; non-metal; solid, black graphite and transparent as diamond; atomic number 6; approximate relative atomic mass 12.

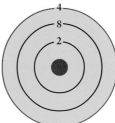

Silicon, from the Latin for flint, 'silex'; chemical symbol Si; Group 4, period 3; metalloid; grey solid; atomic number 14; approximate relative atomic mass 28.

Germanium, from the Latin for Germany, 'Germania'; chemical symbol Ge; Group 4, period 4; metalloid; grey–white solid; atomic number 32; approximate relative atomic mass 73.

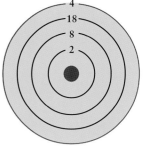

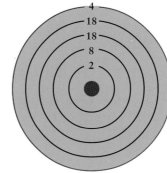

Tin, from the Anglo-Saxon 'tin' and the Latin 'stannum'; chemical symbol Sn; Group 4, period 5; metal; soft silvery-white solid; atomic number 50; approximate relative atomic mass 119.

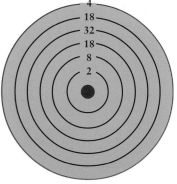

Lead, from the Anglo-Saxon 'lead' and the Latin 'plumbum'; chemical symbol Pb; Group 4, period 6; metal; soft blue–white solid; atomic number 82; approximate relative atomic mass 207.

hydroxide, and this shows that amphoteric properties are found in this group as well as in Group 3.

Some of the elements in Group 4 can form giant molecules (for example, diamond and another form of carbon called buckminsterfullerene – these are called macro-covalent crystals).

Demonstration 1: decomposition of lead carbonate

The metallic character of an element is most evident near the bottom of Group 4. Lead forms typical metallic compounds such as lead hydroxide, lead carbonate and lead nitrate. The compounds of lead are decomposed relatively easily to lead oxide, suggesting that lead is less reactive and less metallic in character than the elements in Groups 1 and 2.

If some white lead carbonate powder is placed in a boiling tube (①) and heated strongly with a Bunsen flame, it decomposes to give off carbon dioxide gas (②). The presence of carbon dioxide can be tested for by fitting the boiling tube with a delivery tube that dips into a test tube containing limewater. As carbon dioxide bubbles through it, the limewater turns cloudy (③).

The remaining lead(I) oxide begins to fuse into the glass (lead oxide being a component of many types of glass). When it cools, it turns from red–orange to a bright yellow colour (④).

EQUATION: Heating lead carbonate
Lead carbonate ⇨ lead oxide + carbon dioxide
$PbCO_3(s) \Rightarrow PbO(s) + CO_2(g)$

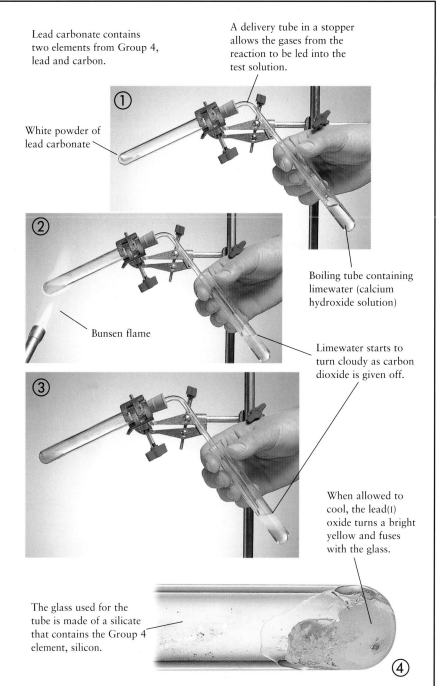

Lead carbonate contains two elements from Group 4, lead and carbon.

A delivery tube in a stopper allows the gases from the reaction to be led into the test solution.

White powder of lead carbonate

Bunsen flame

Boiling tube containing limewater (calcium hydroxide solution)

Limewater starts to turn cloudy as carbon dioxide is given off.

When allowed to cool, the lead(I) oxide turns a bright yellow and fuses with the glass.

The glass used for the tube is made of a silicate that contains the Group 4 element, silicon.

Demonstration 2: carbon can produce giant molecules – polymers

Carbon is unique in that it is able to bond with itself to form stable long chains and rings. It is this property that allows carbon to form so many compounds.

Compounds with long chains of carbon atoms are called POLYMERS. The most abundant organic chemical in the world is a natural polymer of plant fibre called cellulose. One of the products that can be obtained from cellulose is another polymer, rayon, the preparation of which is demonstrated here.

A mixture of green copper(II) carbonate and concentrated ammonia solution are first made up (⑤). This reaction produces indigo blue tetraammine-copper(II) which has the ability to dissolve cellulose.

The source of cellulose for this demonstration is filter paper. The filter paper is cut into strips and simply stirred into the solution of tetraammine-copper(II). It dissolves within a few seconds (⑥).

A small quantity of the dissolved cellulose can now be sucked into a pipette, and then transferred to a Petri dish containing a shallow layer of dilute sulphuric acid. A small part of the dissolved solution can be squirted into the Petri dish, taking care to make sure the pipette does not move. Rayon is immediately precipitated (⑦). As the rayon precipitates, it has to be trapped against the glass bottom of the Petri dish. Once trapped, the pipette can then be drawn slowly through the acid, squeezing gently on the bulb at the same time so that a long filament of rayon is produced.

Better quality rayon threads can be produced industrially and are used in the manufacture of clothing.

(Right) **Carbon produces millions of organic compounds that make the building blocks for living organisms.**
The fossil fuels (gas, oil and coal) are derived from the tissues of plants and animals. These fuels are our principal energy source to heat our homes and drive our machines. But, along with other organic compounds, they are also the chemical resource from which most synthetic materials are manufactured. Many of these synthetic materials (such as plastic) are polymers.

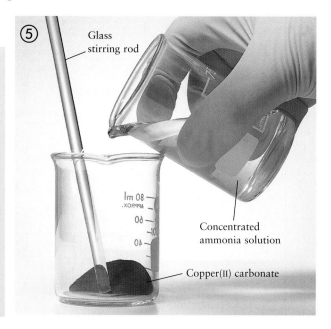

⑤ Glass stirring rod

80 ml APPROX.
60
40

Concentrated ammonia solution

Copper(II) carbonate

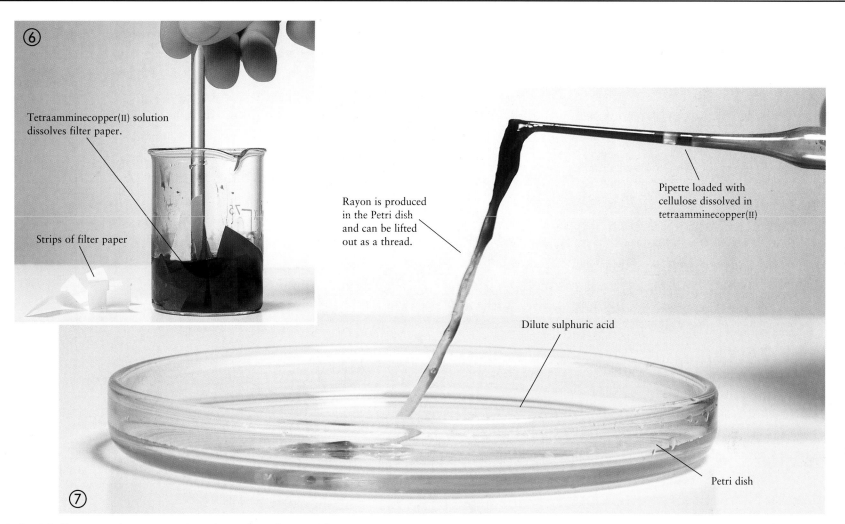

⑥

Tetraamminecopper(II) solution dissolves filter paper.

Strips of filter paper

Rayon is produced in the Petri dish and can be lifted out as a thread.

Pipette loaded with cellulose dissolved in tetraamminecopper(II)

Dilute sulphuric acid

Petri dish

⑦

(Below) A diagrammatic representation of a section of rayon. The rayon polymer can be made of up to 270 glucose units derived from the cellulose.

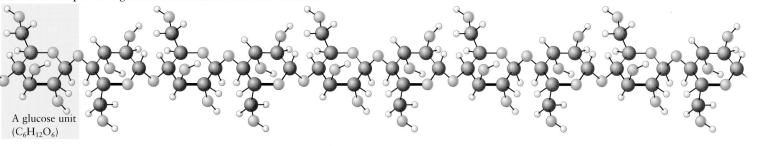

A glucose unit ($C_6H_{12}O_6$)

Group 5 elements

The elements in this group are nitrogen, phosphorus, arsenic, antimony and bismuth, and they are characterised by having five electrons in their outer shells. They are more non-metallic than the Group 4 elements.

Nitrogen is the most common element in this group. It exists in the atmosphere as molecules of two atoms bonded to one another, N_2. It is a very unreactive gas because the energy needed to break the bond between the nitrogen atoms is very large. This also explains why there is so much nitrogen in the atmosphere – it has not reacted to form anything else!

Nitrogen will react with oxygen at high temperatures to form nitrogen monoxide, NO. Nitrogen monoxide is a neutral oxide, and reacts rapidly with more oxygen to form an acidic oxide, nitrogen dioxide, a brown gas. The formation of acidic or neutral oxides is typical non-metal behaviour.

The hydride (substance containing hydrogen) of nitrogen, ammonia (NH_3), is most unusual among the hydrides, in that it is a highly soluble gas and alkaline.

Phosphorus is unusual in that it reacts with alkali to liberate the hydride phosphine which, in the standard preparation, ignites

(Left) **Nitrogen makes up 79% of the atmosphere by volume, and 76% by mass.**

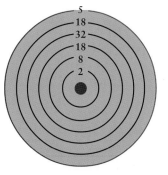

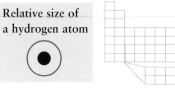

GROUP 5 ELEMENTS

Relative size of a hydrogen atom

Group 5 elements have five electrons in the outer shell

Nitrogen, from the Greek for soda-forming, 'nitron genes'; chemical symbol N; Group 5, period 2; non-metal; colourless gas; atomic number 7; approximate relative atomic mass 14.

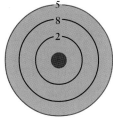

Phosphorus, from the Greek for light producing, 'phosphoros'; chemical symbol P; Group 5, period 3; non-metal; white, red or black solid; atomic number 15; approximate relative atomic mass 31.

Arsenic, from the Greek for a man or male, 'arsenikos'; chemical symbol As; Group 5, period 4; metalloid; grey solid; atomic number 33; approximate relative atomic mass 75.

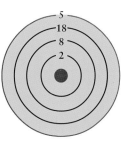

Antimony, from an Arabic word, and the Latin 'stibium'; chemical symbol Sb; Group 5, period 5; metalloid; a soft blue–white solid; atomic number 51; approximate relative atomic mass 122.

Bismuth, from the German for white mass, 'weisse Masse'; chemical symbol Bi; Group 5, period 6; metal; brittle white–pink solid; atomic number 83; approximate relative atomic mass 209.

spontaneously on contact with air and can produce smoke rings of phosphorus oxide.

Phosphorus(V) oxide reacts exothermically with water to form phosphoric acid, a typical non-metal oxide reaction.

Arsenic, antimony and bismuth show an increasingly metallic character at the bottom of the group. They form insoluble sulphides with increasing readiness down the group when hydrogen sulphide gas is bubbled through a solution containing a salt of these elements.

Demonstration 1: the metallic nature of antimony

If hydrochloric acid is added to a sample of antimony metal in a test tube, there appears to be no reaction at all (①). Thus it would appear that antimony is not behaving as a metal.

However, when hydrogen sulphide is bubbled into the colourless solution, a reaction immediately occurs and orange antimony sulphide precipitate is produced (② & ③). This demonstrates that some of the antimony had reacted with the hydrochloric acid to form antimony chloride and so a metallic character is still present in antimony, although it is generally described as a metalloid.

EQUATION 1: Antimony and hydrochloric acid

Antimony + hydrochloric acid ⇨ antimony chloride + hydrogen

$Sb(s) + 2HCl(aq) \rightleftharpoons SbCl_2(aq) + H_2(g)$

EQUATION 2: Antimony chloride and hydrogen sulphide

Antimony chloride + hydrogen sulphide ⇨ antimony sulphide + hydrochloric acid

$SbCl_2(aq) + H_2S(g) \rightleftharpoons SbS(s) + 2HCl(aq)$

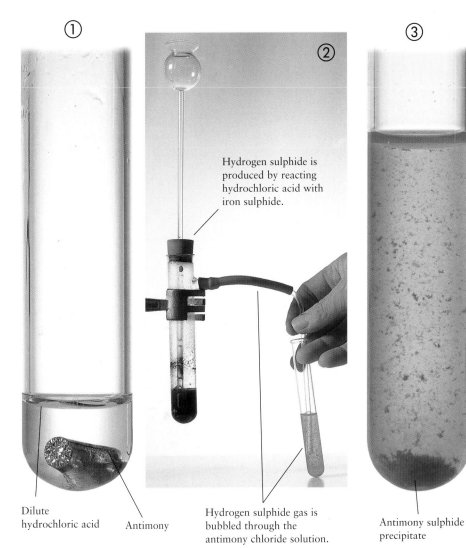

① ② ③

Hydrogen sulphide is produced by reacting hydrochloric acid with iron sulphide.

Dilute hydrochloric acid   Antimony

Hydrogen sulphide gas is bubbled through the antimony chloride solution.

Antimony sulphide precipitate

45

Demonstration 2: phosphorus forms an oxide that is acidic in water, typical behaviour for a non-metal

White phosphorus is an extremely reactive element of Group 5. It is normally kept under water because exposure to air creates rapid oxidation, which quickly results in combustion. This particular form of phosphorus is very unstable because the molecules have formed in such a way that they already contain considerable energy.

Phosphorus is produced as sticks for use in the laboratory, and a small piece is cut off for this demonstration ((4)). The freshly cut end begins smoking almost immediately, and so some speed is necessary when conducting this demonstration to prevent premature ignition.

The apparatus consists of a pneumatic trough containing tap water. A few drops of Universal Indicator are added to the water and stirred to give the resulting solution a bluish colour (this shows that this tap water is slightly alkaline). A crucible lid is fixed to a cork so that, when the piece of phosphorus is placed on the lid, it will float on the water. A bell jar without a stopper is then placed over the floating phosphorus. If the phosphorus is touched with a warm piece of wire ((5)), the phosphorus combusts. The stopper is quickly replaced at the top of the bell jar. The phosphorus burns, reacting with the oxygen and producing a white smoke of phosphorus(V) oxide particles ((6)).

The white phosphorus oxide settles on the water, and as it does so, the colour of the indicator inside the bell jar turns to pink as the phosphorus(V) oxide is dissolved in the water and forms phosphoric acid ((7)). Acidic oxides are typical of non-metals.

EQUATION 1: **Phosphorus burns to produce acidic phosphorus(V) oxide**
Phosphorus + oxygen ⇨ phosphorus(V) oxide
$P_4(s, white) + 5O_2(g) ⇨ P_4O_{10}(s)$

EQUATION 2: **Phosphorus(V) oxide absorbs water to form phosphoric acid**
Phosphorus(V) oxide + water ⇨ phosphoric acid
$P_4O_{10}(s) + 6H_2O(l) ⇨ 4H_3PO_4(aq)$
Heat given out

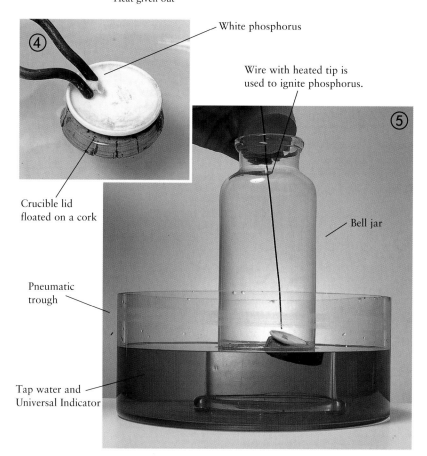

(4)

White phosphorus

Wire with heated tip is used to ignite phosphorus.

(5)

Crucible lid floated on a cork

Bell jar

Pneumatic trough

Tap water and Universal Indicator

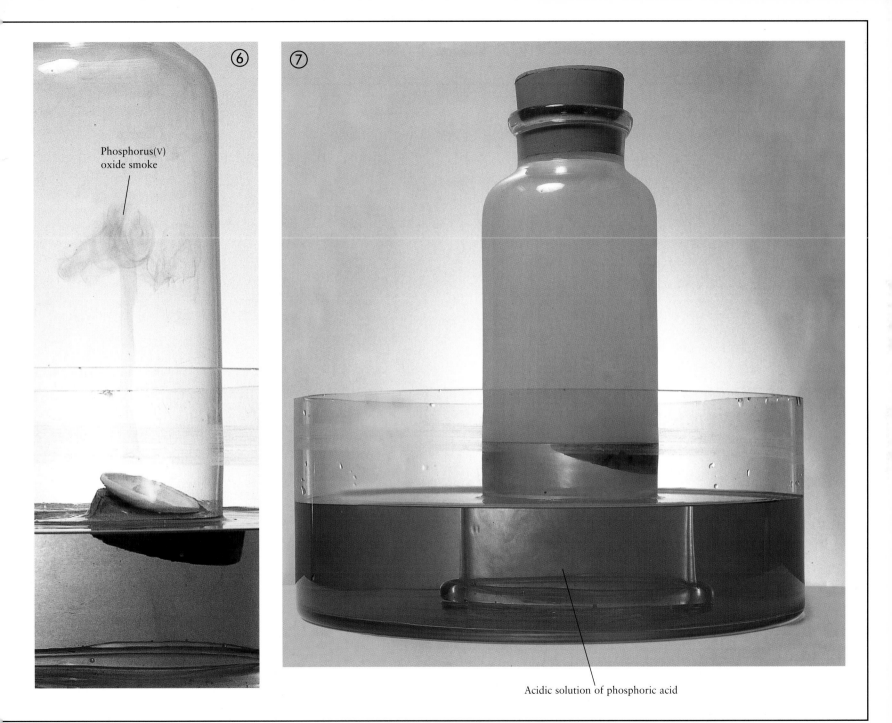

⑥ ⑦

Phosphorus(V) oxide smoke

Acidic solution of phosphoric acid

Demonstration 3: nitrogen forms an oxide that is acidic in water, typical behaviour for a non-metal

Nitrogen dioxide is a poisonous gas, and this demonstration is performed in a fume chamber.

Nitrogen dioxide is prepared by adding concentrated nitric acid to copper turnings (⑧). This is conveniently done by placing the copper turnings in the bottom of a side-arm boiling tube and fitting it with a thistle funnel. When a small amount of concentrated nitric acid is added through the thistle funnel, dense fumes of deep reddish-brown nitrogen dioxide gas are produced.

Nitrogen dioxide produces a very acidic solution when passed over wet pH paper, turning it a deep red (⑨).

However, nitrogen dioxide is also a bleaching agent, and so the bright red colour will fade if gas is played on to the pH paper for some time.

EQUATION 1: Preparing nitrogen dioxide gas for testing for an acid gas
Copper + nitric acid ⇨ *copper nitrate + water + nitrogen dioxide*
$Cu(s) + 4HNO_3(conc) ⇨ Cu(NO_3)_2(aq) + 2H_2O(l) + 2NO_2(g)$

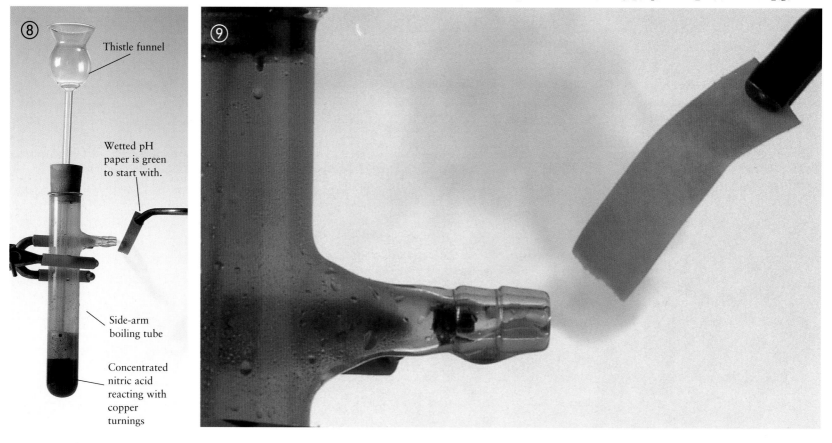

⑧ Thistle funnel

Wetted pH paper is green to start with.

Side-arm boiling tube

Concentrated nitric acid reacting with copper turnings

⑨

Demonstration 4: the reaction of phosphorus with alkalis

The hydrogen compounds of elements in Group 5 decrease in stability down the group. Unlike ammonia gas (NH_3) (see page 50), phosphine (PH_3) is not very soluble in water.

Phosphine is poisonous and so the whole of this demonstration is performed in a fume chamber. White phosphorus is placed in concentrated sodium hydroxide and bubbles of phosphine gas can be seen (⑩).

The gas is prepared in a side-arm boiling tube in the absence of air and passed into a beaker of water (⑪).

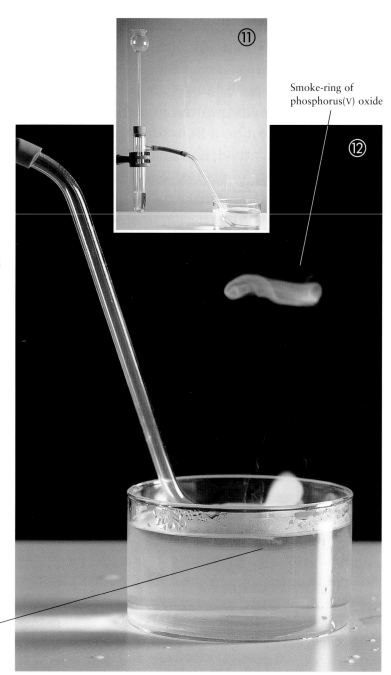

Smoke-ring of phosphorus(V) oxide

The phosphine gas contains an impurity, diphosphine (P_2H_4), which burns spontaneously in air. This creates the flame you see as the gas mixture reaches the surface of the water (⑫).

As the phosphine gas bubbles catch fire, they form solid phosphorus(V) oxide and create white smoke-rings.

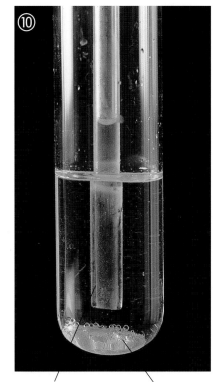

Concentrated sodium hydroxide

White phosphorus

Bubbles of phosphine and diphosphine gas pass through the water and ignite as they burst on reaching the surface.

49

Demonstration 6: nitrogen is an unreactive substance unless a large amount of energy is applied

If a compound containing nitrogen decomposes to form nitrogen gas (N_2) as one of the products, the energy associated with the bond between the two atoms is released, usually very abruptly. As the relative space occupied by a solid is so much less than that occupied by a gas, a sudden change of state of a substance from a solid to a gas creates a rapid expansion, and consequent displacement of whatever material is around that substance in an explosion. As a result, this demonstration is performed in the safety of a fume chamber.

In this demonstration, some crystals of orange ammonium dichromate (⑰) are strongly heated on a ceramic dish. The heating adds energy to the crystals.

The first change is that the surface crystals glow red-hot. At this point, the chemical decomposition of the ammonium dichromate has started and the external heating is removed. The reaction gives out heat as nitrogen molecules form and are released as a gas. Steam is driven off and a much bulkier green solid of chromium oxide is thrown up in the air (⑱).

Whilst the ammonium dichromate continues to decompose, it gives a glowing yellow and white core to what increasingly resembles a volcano (⑲). The chromium oxide 'ash' builds a cone that grows ever higher (⑳).

Remarks

The process of decomposition takes several minutes, giving a spectacular, controlled pyrotechnic display. Once the reaction has got under way, the remainder of the demonstration is best seen in a room with the lighting dimmed.

Orange ammonium dichromate

⑰

⑱

EQUATION: Heating ammonium dichromate
Ammonium dichromate ⇨ nitrogen + chromium oxide + water
$(NH_4)_2Cr_2O_7(s) ⇨ N_2(g) + Cr_2O_3(s) + 4H_2O(g)$

⑲

Green chromium
oxide

The green chromium oxide
produced during the
reaction is much less dense
and therefore occupies
much more space than the
original orange ammonium
dichromate crystals.

⑳

Group 6 elements

The most important elements in this group are oxygen and sulphur, both of which are non-metals. The other elements in this group, selenium, tellurium and polonium (radioactive) are metalloids. Each element is characterised by having six electrons in its outer shell.

Oxygen, sulphur, selenium and tellurium are also known as the CHALCOGENS, a word that comes from the Greek meaning 'brass maker', because all these elements are found in copper ores, and copper is the most important metal in making brass.

The most common member of this group is oxygen, itself the most abundant element in the Earth's crust and which also makes a quarter of the mass and just over a fifth of the volume of the Earth's atmosphere. Oxygen is essential for most living things, and its most important compound is water (H_2O, see page 13).

Oxygen and sulphur combine to form sulphur dioxide SO_2 – an acidic gas, illustrating the non-metal chemistry of sulphur.

(Right) **Oxygen makes up 21% of the atmosphere by volume and 23% by mass. It is produced by plants during photosynthesis and used by living things during respiration.**

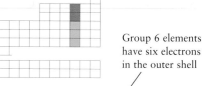

Relative size of a hydrogen atom

Group 6 elements have six electrons in the outer shell

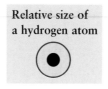

Oxygen, from the Greek for acid forming, 'oxys genes'; chemical symbol O; Group 6, period 2; non-metal; colourless as oxygen gas and dark blue as ozone gas; atomic number 8; approximate relative atomic mass 16.

Sulphur, from the Sanskrit 'sulvere'; chemical symbol S; Group 6, period 3; non-metal; yellow solid; atomic number 16; approximate relative atomic mass 32.

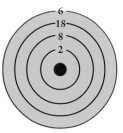

Selenium, from the Greek for the moon, 'selene'; chemical symbol Se; Group 6, period 4; metalloid; grey solid; atomic number 34; approximate relative atomic mass 79.

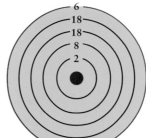

Tellurium, from the Latin for earth, 'tellus'; chemical symbol Te; Group 6, period 5; metalloid; silvery-white solid; atomic number 52; approximate relative atomic mass 128.

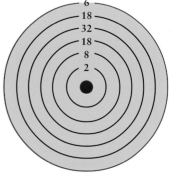

Polonium, named after Poland; chemical symbol Po; Group 6, period 6; metalloid, radioactive; grey solid; atomic number 84; approximate relative atomic mass (209).

Demonstration 1: oxygen dissolves in water and so can oxidise some dissolved substances

Concentrated ammonia solution is added from a pipette to a test tube containing white copper(I) chloride (①). This produces a colourless solution of copper(I) ammine. However, the copper(I) ammine is not stable in air and rapidly oxidises to copper(II) ammine which is a deep indigo-blue colour (②).

The way to see that this effect is produced by oxidation is to leave the tube to stand. Within a few moments, a very deep blue layer begins to form on the surface of the solution that can be reached by the air. The first signs occur in the shape of the meniscus where the liquid meets the air. Over some minutes, air dissolves in the solution to about one and a half centimetres, and thus the blue colour gradually extends into the solution.

If the blue part of the liquid is taken off by using a pipette, the surface part of the solution rapidly returns to being blue as oxidation occurs at the meniscus again.

Remarks

The penetration of oxygen into water, and the very reactive nature of oxygen, are also the reasons that nails rust when left to stand in water (③).

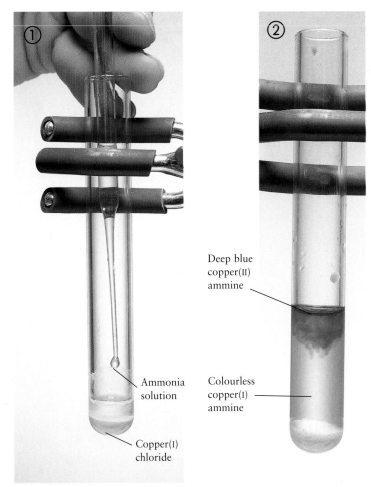

Ammonia solution

Copper(I) chloride

Deep blue copper(II) ammine

Colourless copper(I) ammine

EQUATION: The rusting of iron

Iron + water + oxygen ⇨ *iron(III) hydroxide* ⇨ *iron(III) oxide + water*

$$4Fe(s) + 6H_2O(l) + 3O_2(g) \Rightarrow 4Fe(OH)_3(s) \Rightarrow 2Fe_2O_3(s) + 6H_2O(l)$$

Rust

Demonstration 2: many metals and non-metals combust in oxygen and are oxidised

It is the oxygen in the air that normally supports COMBUSTION. However, air contains only one-fifth oxygen by volume, and so many substances combust much more dramatically, and may burn, when heated in pure oxygen. During combustion with oxygen, the original substance is oxidised to produce oxides. Oxygen is an oxidising agent and so it takes electrons from the original substance.

The temperatures at which combustion occurs in air vary widely between elements. Metals in Group 1 can BURN spontaneously as soon as they come into contact with air. Those in Group 2 combust readily but may need some heating. Metals in Groups 3 and 4, and those in the transition metals such as iron, combust only when heated strongly. Aluminium, for example, only combusts at about 2000°C. Carbon-based substances tend to combust within the temperature range of 300 to 400°C.

(a) a metal: combustion of iron in oxygen

In this demonstration a piece of steel wool is used (④). Steel wool is made of very thin strands of iron and so has a large surface area. This helps speed up the reaction.

A gas jar is filled with oxygen, and the jar is sealed with a glass cover slip. A centimetre or so of water is run into the bottom of the gas jar without losing too much oxygen.

The steel wool is held in metal tongs and heated in a Bunsen flame until it glows red-hot (⑤). The glow is caused by the increase in temperature of iron.

The hot and glowing steel wool is then transferred to the gas jar filled with oxygen (⑥). The iron starts to glow white-hot, showing clearly that the rate of combustion has been increased by the higher concentration of oxygen. The high temperature reached during the reaction causes some steel to melt and droplets are

④

Steel wool

⑤

Gas jar containing oxygen, some water and a glass cover slip

Bunsen burner

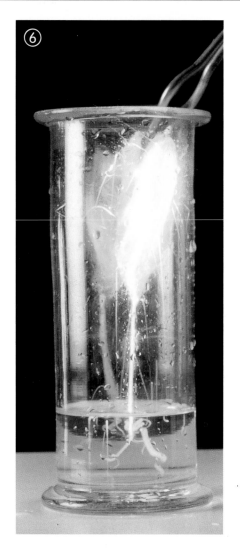

EQUATION: Burning steel wool in oxygen
Iron + oxygen ⇨ iron(III) oxide
$4Fe(s) + 3O_2(g) \Rightarrow 2Fe_2O_3(s)$

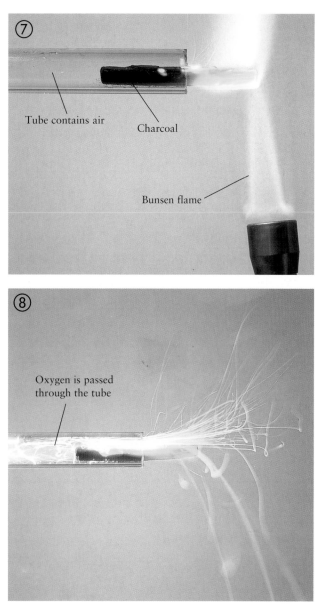

Tube contains air

Charcoal

Bunsen flame

Oxygen is passed through the tube

EQUATION: Burning carbon in oxygen
Carbon + oxygen ⇨ carbon dioxide
$C(s) + O_2(g) \Rightarrow CO_2(g)$

caught safely in the water at the bottom of the gas jar.

Some of the iron has oxidised to iron(III) oxide. As we saw for calcium oxide on page 25, the oxides of metals are basic and some form alkaline solutions. Iron(III) oxide is insoluble but reacts with acid (rust remover).

(b) a non-metal: combustion of carbon in oxygen

In this demonstration, carbon in the form of a small stick of charcoal is placed in the end of a glass tube and heated with a Bunsen flame until it glows white-hot (⑦). The flame is then removed, and the charcoal continues to burn in air with a red glow.

The tube is now connected to a supply of oxygen gas. The charcoal immediately glows white-hot and releases many incandescent particles, both out into the laboratory and back up the glass tube (⑧). The oxygen has increased the rate of combustion. The carbon is oxidised to carbon dioxide gas.

Demonstration 3: sulphur reacts with oxygen to produce an acid gas, sulphur dioxide, typical of non-metals

Oxygen is at the top of Group 6 and is more reactive than sulphur. Hot sulphur will burn in oxygen to produce sulphur dioxide gas (SO_2). As is typical of non-metals, this oxide of sulphur is acidic. However, sulphur dioxide is also poisonous and so this demonstration is conducted in a fume chamber.

The apparatus shown here is similar to that shown for iron on page 56. However, in this case, some sulphur powder is placed on a suitable metal holder – a combustion spoon (⑨). The sulphur is heated in air until it ignites, before being placed in the gas jar.

Notice that the combustion spoon has a metal disc above it in order to protect anyone holding the spoon while the sulphur is burning. The disc also serves as a support for holding the spoon in the middle of the gas jar whilst partly sealing in the gas.

When the burning sulphur is placed in the gas jar filled with oxygen, it burns much more brightly with a characteristic blue flame (⑩).

Sulphur dioxide gas is produced that is acidic. The gas is also a powerful reducing agent, which can be tested for using a strip of dampened filter paper soaked in potassium dichromate. The dichromate is rapidly reduced to a blue–green colour which can appear almost colourless in dilute solution on paper.

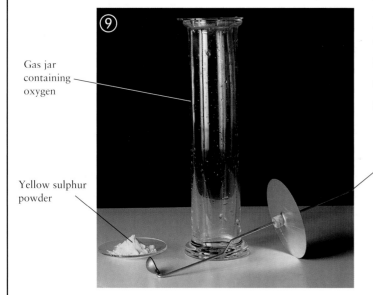

⑨

Gas jar containing oxygen

Yellow sulphur powder

Combustion spoon

EQUATION: Burning sulphur in oxygen
Sulphur + oxygen ⇨ sulphur dioxide
$S(s) + O_2(g) \Rightarrow SO_2(g)$

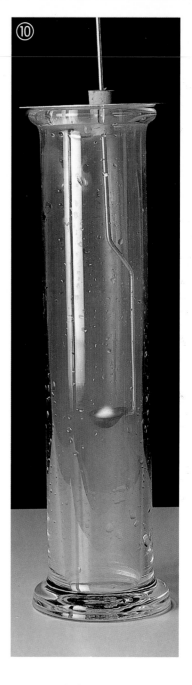

⑩

Demonstration 4: the result of heating copper sulphide

Sulphur is a very reactive non-metal and will combine with most metals. In the absence of oxygen they will form sulphides, and many naturally occurring sulphur compounds are sulphides. Roasting a sulphide in air releases sulphur dioxide gas. The oxygen in the air is more reactive than sulphur and so displaces it from the sulphide as sulphur dioxide.

This demonstration uses some black copper(II) sulphide powder. As sulphur dioxide is a poisonous gas, the demonstration is done in a fume chamber.

The powder is placed in a crucible (⑪) and heated strongly with a Bunsen burner. Shortly after, blue flames appear to dance above the copper sulphide, an indication that sulphur is being liberated and burning to produce sulphur dioxide (⑫). To test for the presence of sulphur dioxide, a piece of filter paper that has been soaked in potassium dichromate is introduced above the hot granules, the dichromate paper changes to blue, which appears almost colourless on the paper, demonstrating that sulphur dioxide gas is being given off.

Filter paper soaked in dichromate

Copper(II) sulphide powder

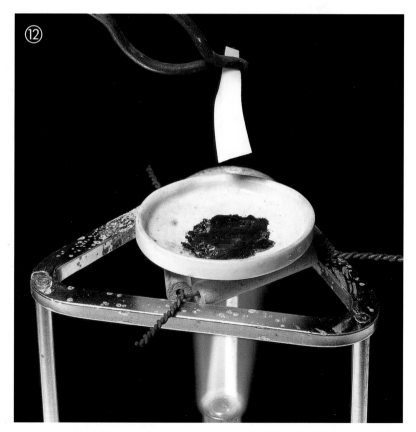

Remarks

Many metal ores are sulphides. They are roasted at higher temperatures to extract the metal oxide.

EQUATION: Heating copper sulphide in air
Copper(II) sulphide + oxygen ⇨ copper(II) oxide + sulphur dioxide
$2CuS(s) + 3O_2(g) ⇨ 2CuO(s) + 2SO_2(g)$

Group 7 elements, the halogens

The elements in this group are non-metals and are known as the HALOGENS. They are all very reactive. The halogens are characterised by having seven electrons in their outer shells. They are fluorine, chlorine, bromine, iodine and astatine (which is radioactive).

To be stable, each of the halogen atoms needs to have eight electrons in its outermost shell. As a result, the atoms react with other elements to gain an electron and fill the shell. The smallest atoms try to fill their electron shell most vigorously, and as fluorine is the smallest of the family, it is the most reactive. Iodine has a much larger atom and is the least reactive of the family.

Fluorine is the most reactive of all elements. It is so highly corrosive and dangerous that it is never used in any school laboratory demonstrations. Because fluorine is so reactive, it is never found free in nature.

The halogens are all powerful oxidising agents. Their oxidising power decreases down the group. This is clearly seen where bromine displaces iodine from a solution of iodide ions and where chlorine displaces bromine from a solution of bromide ions or iodine from a solution of iodide ions.

The silver salts of the halogens are all light sensitive.

Halogen comes from the Greek 'salt producing'. The halogens will react with all metals to form salts. The hydrides of the halogens are all strong acids in aqueous solution. Hydrochloric acid (HCl), for example, is easily prepared by the action of concentrated sulphuric acid (H_2SO_4) on a chloride.

GROUP 7 ELEMENTS, THE HALOGENS

Relative size of a hydrogen atom

Group 7 elements have seven electrons in the outer shell

Fluorine, from the Latin for the phrase to flow – 'fluere'; chemical symbol F; Group 7, period 2; non-metal, halogen; yellow to colourless gas; atomic number 8; approximate relative atomic mass 16.

Chlorine, the Greek for yellowish-green, 'chloros'; chemical symbol Cl; Group 7, period 3; non-metal, halogen; yellow–green gas; atomic number 17; approximate relative atomic mass 35.

Bromine, from the Greek for a foul smell or stench, 'bromos'; chemical symbol Br; Group 7, period 4; non-metal, halogen; red–brown gas; atomic number 35; approximate relative atomic mass 80.

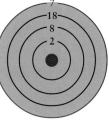

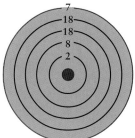

Iodine, from the Greek for the colour violet, 'iodes'; chemical symbol I; Group 7, period 5; non-metal, halogen; violet–black solid or violet gas; atomic number 53; approximate relative atomic mass 127.

Astatine, from the Greek for unstable, 'astatos'; chemical symbol At; Group 7, period 6; metalloid, radioactive; atomic number 85; approximate relative atomic mass (210).

Demonstration 1: the halogens are non-metals and will react with all metals

In this demonstration, chlorine is used as an example of the way that the halogens behave as strong oxidising agents, reacting with all metals. Chlorine is very poisonous and so this demonstration is conducted in a fume chamber.

Chlorine is first prepared by reacting hydrochloric acid with potassium permanganate crystals in a conical flask. A delivery tube leads from the flask to a gas jar. Because chlorine is more dense than air, chlorine can be collected by upward displacement in an upturned gas jar.

A sheet of finely divided copper (Dutch metal) is held between a pair of tongs and introduced to the chlorine in the gas jar (①). The Dutch metal spontaneously combusts, showing chlorine to be a powerful oxidising agent (②).

The reaction produces a dense smoke of fine particles of copper (II) chloride.

The relative reactivity of chlorine and bromine with the Group 3 metal, aluminium, is shown by the demonstrations on pages 38 and 39.

The reaction of chlorine with the more reactive Group 1 metals is extremely violent (③). In this picture, sodium is being burnt in a gas jar of chlorine.

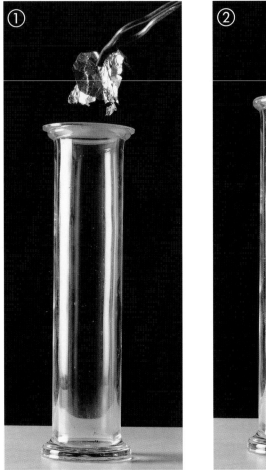

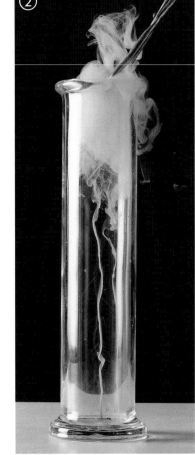

EQUATION: Chlorine reacts with finely divided copper

Chlorine + copper ⇨ copper chloride

$Cl_2(g) + Cu(s) \Rightarrow CuCl_2(s)$

Demonstration 2: halogens are good oxidising agents

In this demonstration, the relative strengths of chlorine, bromine and iodine as oxidising agents are compared. Chlorine and bromine are bubbled into solutions containing ions of the halogens directly below them in the group. Remember that an oxidising agent is a substance that can remove electrons from another substance.

(a) reaction of chlorine with bromide ions

Chlorine is prepared in a conical flask by oxidising hydrochloric acid with potassium permanganate crystals. A delivery tube leads the chlorine gas into a test tube containing colourless potassium bromide solution (④). The solution turns brown (⑤ & ⑥).

In the reaction the chlorine takes electrons from the bromide ions and turns them into bromine atoms, which then form molecules of bromine (which is brown). At the same time, the chlorine molecules gain electrons and become ions. They are then colourless and soluble in water, along with the potassium ions. The demonstration shows that chlorine is a stronger oxidising agent than bromine.

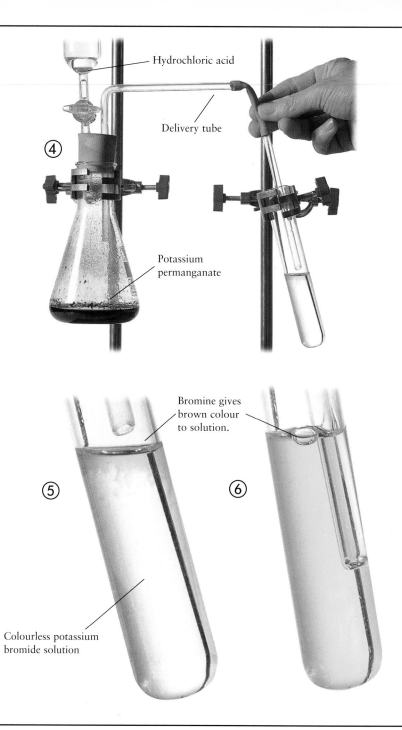

Hydrochloric acid

Delivery tube

④

Potassium permanganate

Bromine gives brown colour to solution.

⑤

⑥

Colourless potassium bromide solution

EQUATION: Oxidation of colourless bromide to solid brown bromine by chlorine

Chlorine + bromide ions ⇨ chloride ions + bromine

$Cl_2(g) + 2Br^-(aq) ⇨ 2Cl^-(aq) + Br_2(s)$

(b) reaction of bromine with iodide ions

A few drops of bromine liquid are placed in a boiling tube, and the tube warmed to vaporise the bromine. A delivery tube takes the bromine gas into a test tube containing colourless potassium iodide (⑦). The solution soon shows black speckles of solid iodine precipitate (⑧).

The bromine oxidises the iodide ions to iodine atoms. This shows that bromine is a stronger oxidising agent than iodine. (The potassium ions are SPECTATOR IONS.)

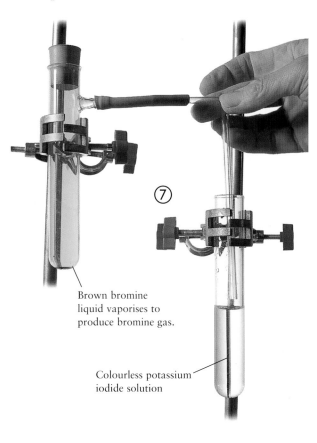

⑦

Brown bromine liquid vaporises to produce bromine gas.

Colourless potassium iodide solution

⑧

Iodine gives brown colour to solution. Particles of solid iodine may form.

EQUATION: Oxidation of colourless iodide ions to solid iodine by bromine

Bromine + iodide ⇨ bromide ions + iodine

$Br_2(g) + 2I^-(aq) ⇨ 2Br^-(aq) + I_2(s)$

Demonstration 3: light causes silver halides to decompose and change colour

This demonstration uses two silver HALIDES, silver bromide and silver chloride, to compare their light-sensitive properties.

Two fresh precipitates are prepared and deposited on filter paper using a suction filter. Because the precipitates are light sensitive, they are prepared in a room with dimmed lighting.

The two precipitates are then placed in Petri dishes (①). The stoppers from two reagent bottles are immediately placed in the centre of each filter paper to protect that part of the silver salt from light so that the change may be observed. The pale yellow precipitate on the left is silver bromide, and the brilliant white precipitate on the right is silver chloride.

After a few minutes in bright light, the precipitate on each filter paper becomes noticeably darker as the silver halides are reduced to silver, due to the effect of light (②).

When the stoppers are taken away, a light-coloured patch remains to show that, where light is excluded, the silver halides remain white (③).

The same principle of a silver salt of a halogen darkening when exposed to light forms the basis of black-and-white photography.

EQUATION: Silver halides are decomposed by sunlight

Silver chloride ⇨ *silver + chlorine*

$$2AgCl(s) \Rightarrow 2Ag(s) + Cl_2(g)$$
Light

Silver chloride ⇨ *silver + chlorine*

$$2AgBr(s) \Rightarrow 2Ag(s) + Br_2(g)$$
Light

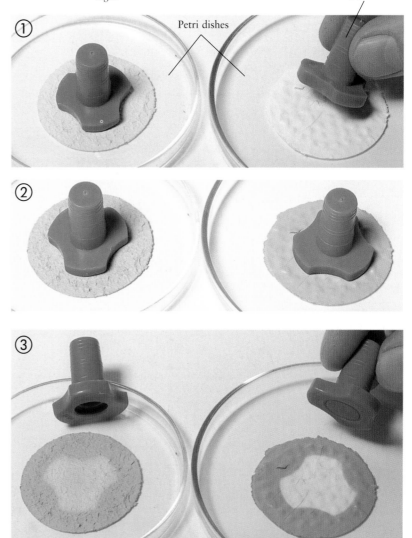

Reagent bottle stopper

Petri dishes

Group 8 elements, the noble gases

The elements in this group are characterised by having a complete set of electrons in their outer shells. This makes them almost entirely unreactive. For this reason, no demonstrations involving the noble gases are shown here.

The members of the group are helium, neon, argon, krypton, xenon and radon. Radon is radioactive.

Helium is the second most abundant element in the Universe after hydrogen but is very rare on Earth because it is so light that its atoms can escape from the Earth's gravitational pull.

All the noble gases are colourless, but emit a coloured light when excited by electricity.

A mixture of argon and nitrogen is used in incandescent light bulbs. When the filament gets hot, it sends out atoms into the bulb. If the bulb contained a reactive gas, the life of the filament would be reduced, and a thin film of metal atoms would be deposited on the inside of the bulb, blackening it and reducing the efficiency of the light.

Argon and nitrogen are inert gases and so do not react within the intensely hot filament. The presence of gas molecules also means that the atoms leaving the filament are more likely to encounter the gas and bounce back on to the filament than they are to reach the glass of the bulb. This prolongs the life of the bulb and stops it from blackening.

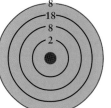

Helium, from the Greek for the Sun, 'helios'; chemical symbol He; non-metal; colourless noble gas; Group 8, period 1; atomic number 2; approximate relative atomic mass 4.

Group 8 elements have a full set of electrons in the outer shell

Neon, from the Greek for new, 'neos'; chemical symbol Ne; non-metal; colourless noble gas; Group 8, period 2; atomic number 10; approximate relative atomic mass 20.

Relative size of a hydrogen atom

Argon, from the Greek for inactive, 'argos'; chemical symbol Ar; non-metal; colourless noble gas; Group 8, period 3; atomic number 18; approximate relative atomic mass 40.

Krypton, from the Greek for hidden, 'kryptos'; chemical symbol Kr; non-metal; colourless noble gas; Group 8, period 4. Atomic number 36, approximate relative atomic mass 84.

Xenon, from the Greek for stranger, 'xenos'; chemical symbol Xe; non-metal; colourless noble gas; Group 8, period 5; atomic number 54; approximate relative atomic mass 131.

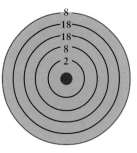

Radon, from radium which is based on the Greek word for ray, 'radius'; chemical symbol Rn; non-metal; colourless noble gas; Group 8, period 6; atomic number 86; approximate relative atomic mass (222).

MASTER GLOSSARY

absolute zero: the lowest possible temperature ($-273.15°C$).

absorption: the process by which a substance is soaked up. *See:* adsorption.

acid: a substance that can give a proton to another substance. Acids are compounds, containing hydrogen, that can attack and dissolve many substances. Acids are described as weak or strong, dilute or concentrated, mineral or organic. *Example:* hydrochloric acid (HCl). An acid in water can react with a base to form a salt and water.

acidic solution: a solution with a pH lower than 7.

acidity: a general term for the strength of an acid in a solution.

acid radical: the negative ion left behind when an acid loses a hydrogen ion. *Example:* Cl^- in hydrochloric acid (HCl).

acid salt: An ACID SALT contains at least one hydrogen ion and can behave as an acid in chemical reactions. Acid salts are produced under conditions that do not allow complete neutralisation of the acid. For example, sulphuric acid may react with a sodium compound to produce a normal sodium salt, sodium sulphate (Na_2SO_4), or it may retain some of the hydrogen, in which case it becomes the salt sodium hydrogen sulphate ($NaHSO_4$).

actinide series or actinide metals: a series of 15 similar radioactive elements between actinium and lawrencium. They are transition metals.

activated charcoal: a form of carbon, made up of tiny crystals of graphite, which is made by heating organic matter in the absence of air. It is then processed further to increase its pore space and therefore its surface area. Its surface area is about 2000 m^2/g. Activated charcoal readily adsorbs many gases and it is therefore widely used as a filter, for example, in gas masks.

activation energy: the energy required to make a reaction occur. The greater the activation energy of a reaction, the more its reaction rate depends on temperature. The activation energy of a reaction is useful because, if the rate of reaction is known at one temperature (for example, 100 °C) then the activation energy can be used to calculate the rate of reaction at another temperature (for example, 400 °C) without actually doing the experiment.

adsorption: the process by which a surface adsorbs a substance. The substances involved are not chemically combined and can be separated. *Example:* the adsorption properties of activated charcoal. *See:* absorption.

alchemy: the traditional 'art' of working with chemicals that prevailed through the Middle Ages. One of the main challenges for alchemists was to make gold from lead. Alchemy faded away as scientific chemistry was developed in the 17th century.

alcohol: an organic compound which contains a hydroxyl (OH) group. *Example:* ethanol (CH_3CH_2OH), also known as ethyl alcohol or grain alcohol.

alkali/alkaline: a base in (aqueous) solution. Alkalis react with, or neutralise, hydrogen ions in acids and have a pH greater than 7.0 because they contain relatively few hydrogen ions. *Example:* aqueous sodium hydroxide (NaOH).

alkaline cell (or battery): a dry cell in which the electrolyte contains sodium or potassium hydroxide.

alkaline earth metal: a member of Group 2 of the Periodic Table. *Example:* calcium.

alkali metals: a member of Group 1 of the Periodic Table. *Example:* sodium.

alkane: a hydrocarbon with no carbon-to-carbon multiple bonds. *Example:* ethane, C_2H_6.

alkene: a hydrocarbon with at least one carbon-to-carbon double bond. *Example:* ethene, C_2H_4.

alkyne: a hydrocarbon with at least one carbon-to-carbon triple bond. *Example:* ethyne, C_2H_2.

allotropes: alternative forms of an element that differ in the way the atoms are linked. *Example:* white and red phosphorus.

alloy: a mixture of a metal and various other elements. *Example:* brass is an alloy of copper and zinc.

amalgam: a liquid alloy of mercury with another metal.

amorphous: a solid in which the atoms are not arranged regularly (i.e. glassy). Compare crystalline.

amphoteric: a metal that will react with both acids and alkalis. *Example:* aluminium metal.

anhydrous: lacking water; water has been removed, for example, by heating. Many hydrated salts are crystalline. (Opposite of anhydrous is hydrous or hydrated.) *Example:* copper(II) sulphate can be anhydrous ($CuSO_4$) or hydrated ($CuSO_4 \cdot 5H_2O$).

anion: a negatively charged atom or group of atoms. *Examples:* chloride ion (Cl^-), hydroxide ion (OH^-).

anode: the electrode at which oxidation occurs; the negative terminal of a battery or the positive electrode of an electrolysis cell.

anodising: a process that uses the effect of electrolysis to make a surface corrosion resistant. *Example:* anodised aluminium.

antacid: a common name for any compound that reacts with stomach acid to neutralise it. *Example:* sodium hydrogen carbonate, also known as sodium bicarbonate.

antioxidant: a substance that reacts rapidly with radicals thereby preventing oxidation of some other substance.

anti-bumping granules: small glass or ceramic beads, designed to promote boiling without the development of large gas bubbles.

approximate relative atomic mass: *See:* relative atomic mass.

aqueous: a solution in which the solvent is water. Usually used as 'aqueous solution'. *Example:* aqueous solution of sodium hydroxide (NaOH(aq)).

aromatic hydrocarbons: compounds of carbon that have the benzene ring as part of their structure. *Examples:* benzene (C_6H_6), naphthalene ($C_{10}H_8$). They are known as aromatic because of the strong pungent smell given off by benzene.

atmospheric pressure: the pressure exerted by the gases in the air. Units of measurement are kilopascals (kPa), atmospheres (atm), millimetres of mercury (mm Hg) and Torr. Standard atmospheric pressure is 100 kPa, 1atm, 760 mm Hg or 760 Torr.

atom: the smallest particle of an element; a nucleus and its surrounding electrons.

atomic mass: the mass of an atom measured in atomic mass units (amu). An atomic mass unit is equal to one-twelfth of the atom of carbon-12. Atomic mass is now more generally used instead of atomic weight. *Example:* the atomic mass of chlorine is about 35 amu. *See:* atomic weight, relative atomic mass.

atomic number: also known as proton number. The number of electrons or the number of protons in an atom. *Example:* the atomic number of gold is 79 and for carbon it is 4.

atomic structure: the nucleus and the arrangement of electrons around the nucleus of an atom.

atomic weight: a common term used to mean the average molar mass of an element. This is the mass per mole of atoms. *Example:* the atomic weight of chlorine is about 35 g/mol. *See:* atomic mass, mole.

base: a substance that can accept a proton from another substance. *Example:* aqueous ammonia ($NH_3(aq)$). A base can react with an acid in water to form a salt and water.

basic salt: a salt that contains at least one hydroxide ion. The hydroxide ion can then behave as a base in chemical reactions. *Example:* the reaction of hydrochloric acid (HCl) with the base, aluminium hydroxide ($Al(OH)_3$) can form two basic salts, $Al(OH)_2Cl$ and $Al(OH)Cl_2$.

battery: a number of electrochemical cells placed in series.

bauxite: a hydrated impure oxide of aluminium ($Al_2O_3 \bullet xH_2O$, with the amount of water x being variable). It is the main ore used to obtain aluminium metal. The reddish-brown colour of bauxite is mainly caused by the iron oxide impurities it contains.

beehive shelf: an inverted earthenware bowl with a hole in the upper surface and a slot in the rim. Traditionally, the earthenware was brown and looked similar to a beehive, hence its name. A delivery tube passes through the slot and a gas jar is placed over the hole. This provides a convenient way to collect gas over water in a pneumatic trough.

bell jar: a tall glass jar with an open bottom and a wide, stoppered neck that is used in conjunction with a beehive shelf and a pneumatic trough in some experiments involving gases. The name derives from historic versions of the apparatus, which resembled a bell in shape.

blast furnace: a tall furnace charged with a mixture of iron ore, coke and limestone and used for the refining of iron metal. The name comes from the strong blast of air introduced during smelting.

bleach: a substance that removes colour in stains on materials, either by oxidising or reducing the staining compound. *Example:* sulphur dioxide (SO_2).

block: one of the main divisions of the Periodic Table. Blocks are named for the outermost, occupied electron shell of an element. *Example:* The Transition Metals all belong to the d-block.

boiling point: the temperature at which a liquid boils, changing from a liquid to a gas. Boiling points change with atmospheric pressure. *Example:* The boiling point of pure water at standard atmospheric pressure is 100 °C.

boiling tube: A thin glass tube closed at one end and used for chemical tests, etc. The composition and thickness of the glass is such that it cannot sustain very high temperatures and is intended for heating liquids to boiling point. *See:* side-arm boiling tube, test tube.

bond: chemical bonding is either a transfer or sharing of electrons by two or more atoms. There are a number of types of chemical bond, some very strong (such as covalent and ionic bonds), others weak (such as hydrogen bonds). Chemical bonds form because the linked molecule is more stable than the unlinked atoms from which it formed. *Example:* the hydrogen molecule (H_2) is more stable than single atoms of hydrogen, which is why hydrogen gas is always found as molecules of two hydrogen atoms.

Boyle's Law: At constant temperature, and for a given mass of gas, the volume of the gas (V) is inversely proportional to pressure that builds up (P): $P \propto 1/V$.

brine: a solution of salt (sodium chloride, NaCl) in water.

Büchner flask: a thick-walled side-arm flask designed to withstand the changes in pressure that occur when the flask is connected to a suction pump.

Büchner funnel: a special design of plastic or ceramic funnel which has a flat stage on which a filter paper can be placed. It is intended for use under suction with a Büchner funnel.

buffer (solution): a mixture of substances in solution that resists a change in the acidity or alkalinity of the solution when small amounts of an acid or alkali are added.

burette: a long, graduated glass tube with a tap at one end. A burette is used vertically, with the tap lowermost. Its main use is as a reservoir for a chemical during titration.

burn: a combustion reaction in which a flame is produced. A flame occurs where *gases* combust and release heat and light. At least two gases are therefore required if there is to be a flame. *Example:* methane gas (CH_4) burns in oxygen gas (O_2) to produce carbon dioxide (CO_2) and water (H_2O) and give out heat and light.

calorimeter: an insulated container designed to prevent heat gain or loss with the environment and thus allow changes of temperature within reacting chemicals to be measured accurately. It is named after the old unit of heat, the calorie.

capillary: a very small diameter (glass) tube. Capillary tubing has a small enough diameter to allow surface tension effects to retain water within the tube.

capillary action: the tendency for a liquid to be sucked into small spaces, such as between objects and through narrow-pore tubes. The force to do this comes from surface tension.

carbohydrate: a compound containing only carbon, hydrogen and oxygen. Carbohydrates have the formula $C_n(H_2O)_n$, where n is variable. *Example:* glucose ($C_6H_{12}O_6$).

carbonate: a salt of carbonic acid. Carbonate ions have the chemical formula CO_3^{2-}. *Examples:* calcium nitrate $CaCO_3$ and sodium carbonate Na_2CO_3.

catalyst: a substance that speeds up a chemical reaction, but itself remains unaltered at the end of the reaction. *Example:* copper in the reaction of hydrochloric acid with zinc.

catalytic converter: a device incorporated into some exhaust systems. The catalytic converter contains a framework and/or granules with a very large surface area and coated with catalysts that convert the pollutant gases passing over them into harmless products.

cathode: the electrode at which reduction occurs; the positive terminal of a battery or the negative electrode of an electrolysis cell.

cathodic protection: the technique of protecting a metal object by connecting it to a more readily oxidisable metal. The metal object being protected is made into the cathode of a cell. *Example:* iron can be protected by coupling it with magnesium. Iron forms the cathode and magnesium the anode.

cation: a positively charged ion. *Examples:* calcium ion (Ca^{2+}), ammonium ion (NH_4^+).

caustic: a substance that can cause burns if it touches the skin. *Example:* Sodium hydroxide, caustic soda (NaOH).

Celsius scale (°C): a temperature scale on which the freezing point of water is at 0 degrees and the normal boiling point at standard atmospheric pressure is 100 degrees.

cell: a vessel containing two electrodes and an electrolyte that can act as an electrical conductor.

centrifuge: an instrument for spinning small samples very rapidly. The fast spin causes the components of a mixture that have a different density to separate. This has the same effect as filtration.

ceramic: a material based on clay minerals which has been heated so that it has chemically hardened.

chalcogens: the members of Group 6 of the Periodic Table: oxygen, sulphur, selenium and tellurium. The word comes from the Greek meaning 'brass giver', because all these elements are found in copper ores, and copper is the most important metal in making brass.

change of state: a change between two of the three states of matter, solid, liquid and gas. *Example:* when water evaporates it changes from a liquid to a gaseous state.

Charles's Law: The volume (V) of a given mass of gas at constant pressure is directly proportional to its absolute temperature (T): $V \propto T$.

chromatography: A separation technique uses the ability of surfaces to adsorb substances with different strengths. The substances with the least adherence to the surface move faster and leave behind those that adhere more strongly.

coagulation: a term describing the tendency of small particles to stick together in clumps.

coherent: meaning that a substance holds together or sticks together well, and without holes or other defects. *Example:* Aluminium appears unreactive because, as soon as new metal is exposed to air, it forms a very complete oxide coating, which then stops further reaction occurring.

coinage metals: the elements copper, silver and gold, used to make coins.

coke: a solid substance left after the gases have been extracted from coal.

colloid: a mixture of ultramicroscopic particles dispersed uniformly through a second substance to form a suspension which may be almost like a solution or may set to a jelly (gel). The word comes from the Greek for glue.

colorimeter: an instrument for measuring the light-absorbing power of a substance. The absorption gives an accurate indication of the concentration of some coloured solutions.

combustion: a reaction in which an element or compound is oxidised to release energy. Some combustion reactions are slow, such as the combustion of the sugar we eat to provide our energy. If the combustion results in a flame, it is called burning. A flame occurs where *gases* combust and release heat and light. At least two gases are therefore required if there is to be a flame. *Example:* the combustion or burning of methane gas (CH_4) in oxygen gas (O_2) produces carbon dioxide (CO_2) and water (H_2O) and gives out heat and light. Some combustion reactions produce light and heat but do not produce flames. *Example:* the combustion of carbon in oxygen produces an intense red–white light but no flame.

combustion spoon: also known as a deflagrating spoon, it consists of a long metal handle with a small cup at the end. Its purpose is to allow the safe introduction of a (usually heated) substance into a gas jar filled with gas, when the reaction is likely to be vigorous. *Example:* the introduction of a heated sodium pellet into a gas jar containing chlorine.

compound: a chemical consisting of two or more elements chemically bonded together. *Example:* Calcium atoms can combine with carbon atoms and oxygen atoms to make calcium carbonate ($CaCO_3$), a compound of all three atoms.

condensation: the formation of a liquid from a gas. This is a change of state, also called a phase change.

condensation nuclei: microscopic particles of dust, salt and other materials suspended in the air, that attract water molecules. The usual result is the formation of water droplets.

condensation polymer: a polymer formed by a chain of reactions in which a water molecule is eliminated as every link of the polymer is formed. *Examples:* polyesters, proteins, nylon.

conduction: (i) the exchange of heat (heat conduction) by contact with another object, or (ii) allowing the flow of electrons (electrical conduction).

conductivity: the ability of a substance to conduct. The conductivity of a solution depends on there being suitable free ions in the solution. A conducting solution is called an electrolyte. *Example:* dilute sulphuric acid.

convection: the exchange of heat energy with the surroundings produced by the flow of a fluid due to being heated or cooled.

corrosion: the oxidation of a metal. Corrosion is often regarded as unwanted and is more generally used to refer to the *slow* decay of a metal resulting from contact with gases and liquids in the environment. *Example:* Rust is the corrosion of iron.

corrosive: causing corrosion. *Example:* Sodium hydroxide ($NaOH$).

covalent bond: this is the most common form of strong chemical bonding and occurs when two atoms *share* electrons. *Example:* oxygen (O_2)

cracking: breaking down complex molecules into simpler compounds, as in oil refining.

crucible: a small bowl with a lip, made of heat-resistant white glazed ceramic. It is used for heating substances using a Bunsen flame.

crude oil: a chemical mixture of petroleum liquids. Crude oil forms the raw material for an oil refinery.

crystal: a substance that has grown freely so that it can develop external faces. Compare crystalline, where the atoms are not free to form individual crystals and amorphous, where the atoms are arranged irregularly.

crystalline: a solid in which the atoms, ions or molecules are organised into an orderly pattern without distinct crystal faces. *Examples:* copper(II) sulphate, sodium chloride. Compare amorphous.

crystallisation: the process in which a solute comes out of solution slowly and forms crystals. *See:* water of crystallisation.

crystal systems: seven patterns or systems into which all crystals can be grouped: cubic, hexagonal, rhombohedral, tetragonal, orthorhombic, monoclinic and triclinic.

cubic crystal system: groupings of crystals that look like cubes.

current: an electric current is produced by a flow of electrons through a conducting solid or ions through a conducting liquid. The rate of supply of this charge is measured in amperes (A).

decay (radioactive decay): the way that a radioactive element changes into another element due to loss of mass through radiation. *Example:* uranium 238 decays with the loss of an alpha particle to form thorium 234.

decomposition: the break down of a substance (for example, by heat or with the aid of a catalyst) into simpler components. In such a chemical reaction only one substance is involved. *Example:* hydrogen peroxide ($H_2O_2(aq)$) into oxygen ($O_2(g)$) and water ($H_2O(l)$).

decrepitation: when, as part of the decomposition of a substance, cracking sounds are also produced. *Example:* heating of lead nitrate ($Pb(NO_3)_2$).

dehydration: the removal of water from a substance by heating it, placing it in a dry atmosphere or using a drying (dehydrating) reagent such as concentrated sulphuric acid.

density: the mass per unit volume (e.g. g/cc).

desalinisation: the removal of all the salts from sea water, by reverse osmosis or heating the water and collecting the distillate. It is a very energy-intensive process.

desiccant: a substance that absorbs water vapour from the air. *Example:* silica gel.

desiccator: a glass bowl and lid containing a shelf. The apparatus is designed to store materials in dry air. A desiccant is placed below the shelf and the substance to be dried is placed on the shelf. The lid makes a gas-tight joint with the bowl.

destructive distillation: the heating of a material so that it decomposes entirely to release all of its volatile components. Destructive distillation is also known as pyrolysis.

detergent: a chemical based on petroleum that removes dirt.

Devarda's alloy: zinc with a trace of copper, which acts as a catalyst for reactions with the zinc.

diaphragm: a semipermeable membrane – a kind of ultrafine mesh filter – that allows only small ions to pass through. It is used in the electrolysis of brine.

diffusion: the slow mixing of one substance with another until the two substances are evenly mixed. Mixing occurs because of differences in concentration within the mixture. Diffusion works rapidly with gases, very slowly with liquids.

diffusion combustion: the form of combustion that occurs when two gases only begin to mix during ignition. As a result the flame is hollow and yellow in colour. *Example:* a candle flame.

dilute acid: an acid whose concentration has been reduced in a large proportion of water.

disinfectant: a chemical that kills bacteria and other microorganisms.

displacement reaction: a reaction that occurs because metals differ in their reactivity. If a more reactive metal is placed in a solution of a less reactive metal compound, a reaction occurs in which the more reactive metal displaces the metal ions in the solution. *Example:* when zinc metal is introduced into a solution of copper(II) sulphate (which thus contains copper ions), zinc goes into solution as zinc ions, while copper is displaced from the solution and forced to precipitate as metallic copper.

dissociate: to break bonds apart. In the case of acids, it means to break up, forming hydrogen ions. This is an example of ionisation. Strong acids dissociate completely. Weak acids are not completely ionised, and a solution of a weak acid has a relatively low concentration of hydrogen ions.

dissolve: to break down a substance in a solution without causing a reaction.

distillation: the process of separating mixtures by condensing the vapours through cooling.

distilled water: distilled water is nearly pure water and is produced by distillation of tap water. Distilled water is used in the laboratory in preference to tap water because the distillation process removes many of the impurities in tap water that may influence the chemical reactions for which the water is used.

Dreschel bottle: a tall bottle with a special stopper, designed to allow a gas to pass through a liquid. The stopper contains both inlet and outlet tubes. One tube extends below the surface of the liquid so that the gas has to pass through the liquid before it can escape to the outlet tube.

dropper funnel: a special funnel with a tap to allow the controlled release of a liquid. Also known as a dropping funnel or tap funnel.

drying agent: *See:* dehydrating agent.

dye: a coloured substance that will stick to another substance so that both appear coloured.

effervesce: to give off bubbles of gas.

effloresce: to lose water and turn to a fine powder on exposure to the air. *Example:* Sodium carbonate on the rim of a reagent bottle stopper.

electrical conductivity: *See:* conductivity

electrical potential: the energy produced by an electrochemical cell and measured by the voltage or electromotive force (emf). *See:* potential difference, electromotive force.

electrochemical cell: a cell consisting of two electrodes and an electrolyte. It can be set up to generate an electric current (usually known as a galvanic cell, an example of which is a battery), or an electric current can be passed through it to produce a chemical reaction (in which case it is called an electrolytic cell and can be used to refine metals or for electroplating).

electrochemical series: the arrangement of substances that are either oxidising or reducing agents in order of strength as a reagent, for example, with the strong oxidising agents at the top of the list and the strong reducing agents at the bottom.

electrode: a conductor that forms one terminal of a cell.

electrolysis: an electrical–chemical process that uses an electric current to cause the break-up of a compound and the movement of metal ions in a solution. The process happens in many natural situations (as for example in rusting) and is also commonly used

in industry for purifying (refining) metals or for plating metal objects with a fine, even metal coating.

electrolyte: an ionic solution that conducts electricity.

electrolytic cell: *See:* electrochemical cell.

electromotive force (emf): the force set up in an electric circuit by a potential difference.

electron: a tiny, negatively charged particle that is part of an atom. The flow of electrons through a solid material such as a wire produces an electric current.

electron configuration: the pattern in which electrons are arranged in shells around the nucleus of an atom. *Example:* chlorine has the configuration 2, 8, 7.

electroplating: depositing a thin layer of a metal on to the surface of another substance using electrolysis.

element: a substance that cannot be decomposed into simpler substance by chemical means. *Examples:* calcium, iron, gold.

emulsion: tiny droplets of one substance dispersed in another. One common oil in water emulsion is called milk. Because the tiny droplets tend to come together, another stabilising substance is often needed. Soaps and detergents are such agents, wrapping the particles of grease and oil in a stable coat. Photographic film is an example of a solid emulsion.

endothermic reaction: a reaction that takes in heat. *Example:* when ammonium chloride is dissolved in water.

end point: the stage in a titration when the reaction between the titrant (added from a burette) and the titrate (in the flask) is complete. The end point is normally recognised by use of an indicator which has been added to

the titrate. In an acid–base reaction this is also called the neutralisation point.

enzyme: biological catalysts in the form of proteins in the body that speed up chemical reactions. Every living cell contains hundreds of enzymes that help the processes of life continue.

ester: organic compounds formed by the reaction of an alcohol with an acid and which often have a fruity taste. *Example:* ethyl acetate ($CH_3COOC_2H_5$).

evaporation: the change of state of a liquid to a gas. Evaporation happens below the boiling point and is used as a method of separating the materials in a solution.

excess, to: if a reactant has been added to another reactant in excess, it has exceeded the amount required to complete the reaction.

exothermic reaction: a reaction that gives out substantial amounts of heat. *Example:* sucrose and concentrated sulphuric acid.

explosive: a substance which, when a shock is applied to it, decomposes very rapidly, releasing a very large amount of heat and creating a large volume of gases as a shock wave.

fats: semisolid, energy-rich compounds derived from plants or animals, made of carbon, hydrogen and oxygen. These are examples of esters.

ferment: to break down a substance by microorganisms in the absence of oxygen. *Example:* fermentation of sugar to ethanol during the production of alcoholic drinks.

filtrate: the liquid that has passed through a filter.

filtration: the separation of a liquid from a solid using a membrane with small holes (i.e. a filter paper).

flame: a mixture of gases undergoing burning. A solid or liquid must produce a gas before it can react with oxygen and burn with a flame.

flammable (also inflammable): able to burn (in air). *Opposite:* non-flammable.

flocculation: the grouping together of small particles in a suspension to form particles large enough to settle out as a precipitate. Flocculation is usually caused by the presence of a flocculating agent. *Example:* calcium ions are the flocculating agent for suspended clay particles.

fluid: able to flow; either a liquid or a gas.

fluorescent: a substance that gives out visible light when struck by invisible waves, such as ultraviolet rays.

flux: a material used to make it easier for a liquid to flow. A flux dissolves metal oxides and so prevents a metal from oxidising while being heated.

foam: a substance that is sufficiently gelatinous to be able to contain bubbles of gas. The gas bulks up the substance, making it behave as though it were semirigid.

fossil fuels: hydrocarbon compounds that have been formed from buried plant and animal remains. High pressures and temperatures lasting over millions of years are required. *Examples:* The fossil fuels are coal, oil and natural gas.

fraction: a group of similar components of a mixture. *Example:* In the petroleum industry the light fractions of crude oil are those with the smallest molecules, while the medium and heavy fractions have larger molecules.

fractional distillation: the separation of the components of a liquid mixture by heating them to their boiling points.

fractionating column: a glass column designed to allow different fractions to be separated when they boil. In industry, it may be called a fractionating tower.

free radical: a very reactive atom or group with a 'spare' electron. *Example:* methyl, $CH_3\bullet$.

freezing point: the temperature at which a substance undergoes a phase change from a liquid to a solid. It is the same temperature as the melting point.

fuel: a concentrated form of chemical energy. The main sources of fuels (called fossil fuels because they were formed by geological processes) are coal, crude oil and natural gas.

fuel rods: the rods of uranium or other radioactive material used as a fuel in nuclear power stations.

fume chamber or fume cupboard: a special laboratory chamber fitted with a protective glass shield and containing a powerful extraction fan to remove toxic fumes.

fuming: an unstable liquid that gives off a gas. Very concentrated acid solutions are often fuming solutions. *Example:* fuming nitric acid.

galvanising: applying a thin zinc coating to protect another metal.

gamma rays: waves of radiation produced as the nucleus of a radioactive element rearranges itself into a tighter cluster of protons and neutrons. Gamma rays carry enough energy to damage living cells.

gangue: the unwanted material in an ore.

gas/gaseous phase: a form of matter in which the molecules form no definite shape and are free to move about to uniformly fill any vessel they are put in. A gas can easily be compressed into a much smaller volume.

gas syringe: a glass syringe with a graduated cylinder designed to collect and measure small amounts of gases produced during an experiment.

gelatinous precipitate: a precipitate that has a jelly-like appearance. *Example:* iron (III) hydroxide. Because a gelatinous precipitate is mostly water, it is of a similar density to water and will float or lie suspended in the liquid. *See:* granular precipitate.

glass: a transparent silicate without any crystal growth. It has a glassy lustre and breaks with a curved fracture. Note that some minerals have all these features and are therefore natural glasses. Household glass is a synthetic silicate.

glucose: the most common of the natural sugars ($C_6H_{12}O_6$). It occurs as the polymer known as cellulose, the fibre in plants. Starch is also a form of glucose.

granular precipitate: a precipitate that has a grain-like appearance. *Example:* lead(II) hydroxide. *See:* gelatinous precipitate.

gravimetric analysis: a quantitative form of analysis in which the mass (weight) of the reactants and products is measured.

group: a vertical column in the Periodic Table. There are eight groups in the table. Their numbers correspond to the number of electrons in the outer shell of the atoms in the group. *Example:* Group 1: member, sodium.

Greenhouse Effect: an increase in the global air temperature as a result of heat released from burning fossil fuels being absorbed by carbon dioxide in the atmosphere.

Greenhouse gas: any of various the gases that contribute to the Greenhouse Effect. *Example:* carbon dioxide.

half-life: the time it takes for the radiation coming from a sample of a radioactive element to decrease by half.

halide: a salt of one of the halogens.

halogen: one of a group of elements including chlorine, bromine, iodine and fluorine in Group 7 of the Periodic Table.

heat: the energy that is transferred when a substance is at a different temperature to that of its surroundings. *See:* endothermic and exothermic reactions.

heat capacity: the ratio of the heat supplied to a substance, compared with the rise in temperature that is produced.

heat of combustion: the amount of heat given off by a mole of a substance during combustion. This heat is a property of the substance and is the same no matter what kind of combustion is involved. *Example:* heat of combustion of carbon is 94.05 kcal (x 4.18 = 393.1 kJ).

hydrate: a solid compound in crystalline form that contains water molecules. Hydrates commonly form when a solution of a soluble salt is evaporated. The water that forms part of a hydrate crystal is known as the 'water of crystallisation'. It can usually be removed by heating, leaving an anhydrous salt.

hydration: the process of absorption of water by a substance. In some cases hydration makes the substance change colour; in many other cases there is no colour change, simply a change in volume. *Example:* dark blue hydrated copper(II) sulphate ($CuSO_4 \cdot 5H_2O$) can be heated to produce white anhydrous copper(II) sulphate ($CuSO_4$).

hydride: a compound containing just hydrogen and another element, most often a metal.

Examples: water (H_2O), methane (CH_4) and phosphine (PH_3).

hydrous: hydrated with water.*See:* anhydrous.

hydrocarbon: a compound in which only hydrogen and carbon atoms are present. Most fuels are hydrocarbons, as is the simple plastic, polyethene. *Example:* methane CH_4.

hydrogen bond: a type of attractive force that holds one molecule to another. It is one of the weaker forms of intermolecular attractive force. *Example:* hydrogen bonds occur in water.

ignition temperature: the temperature at which a substance begins to burn.

immiscible: will not mix with another substance. e.g., oil and water.

incandescent: glowing or shining with heat. *Example:* tungsten filament in an incandescent light bulb.

incomplete combustion: combustion in which only some of the reactant or reactants combust, or the products are not those that would be obtained if all the reactions went to completion. It is uncommon for combustion to be complete and incomplete combustion is more frequent. *Example:* incomplete combustion of carbon in oxygen produces carbon monoxide and not carbon dioxide.

indicator (acid–base indicator): a substance or mixture of substances used to test the acidity or alkalinity of a substance. An indicator changes colour depending on the acidity of the solution being tested. Many indicators are complicated organic substances. Some indicators used in the laboratory include Universal Indicator, litmus, phenolphthalein, methyl orange and bromothymol. *See:* Universal Indicator.

induction period: the time taken for a reaction to reach ignition temperature. During this period, no apparent reaction occurs, then the materials appear to undergo spontaneous combustion.

inert: unreactive.

inhibitor: a substance that prevents a reaction from occurring.

inorganic substance: a substance that does not contain carbon and hydrogen. *Examples:* NaCl, $CaCO_3$.

insoluble: a substance that will not dissolve.

ion: an atom, or group of atoms, that has gained or lost one or more electrons and so developed an electrical charge. Ions behave differently from electrically neutral atoms and molecules. They can move in an electric field, and they can also bind strongly to solvent molecules such as water. Positively charged ions are called cations; negatively charged ions are called anions. Ions can carry an electrical current through solutions.

ionic bond: the form of bonding that occurs between two ions when the ions have opposite charges. *Example:* sodium cations bond with chloride anions to form common salt (NaCl) when a salty solution is evaporated. Ionic bonds are strong bonds except in the presence of a solvent. *See:* bond.

ionic compound: a compound that consists of ions. *Example:* NaCl.

ionise: to break up neutral molecules into oppositely charged ions or to convert atoms into ions by the loss of electrons.

ionisation: a process that creates ions.

isotope: an atom that has the same number of protons in its nucleus, but which has a different mass. *Example:* carbon 12 and carbon 14.

Kipp's apparatus: a piece of glassware consisting of three

chambers, designed to provide a continuous and regulated production of gas by bringing the reactants into contact in a controlled way.

lanthanide series or lanthanide metals: a series of 15 similar metallic elements between lanthanum and lutetium. They are transition metals and also also called rare earths.

latent heat: the amount of heat that is absorbed or released during the process of changing state between gas, liquid or solid. For example, heat is absorbed when a substance melts and it is released again when the substance solidifies.

lattice: a regular arrangement of atoms, ions or molecules in a crystalline solid.

leaching: the extraction of a substance by percolating a solvent through a material. *Example:* when water flows through an ore, some of the heavy metals in it may be leached out causing environmental pollution.

Liebig condenser: a piece of glassware consisting of a sloping water-cooled tube. The design allows a volatile material to be condensed and collected.

liquefaction: to make something liquid.

liquid/liquid phase: a form of matter that has a fixed volume but no fixed shape.

lime (quicklime): calcium oxide (CaO). A white, caustic solid, manufactured by heating limestone and used for making mortar, fertiliser or bleach.

limewater: an aqueous solution of calcium hydroxide, used especially to detect the presence of carbon dioxide.

litmus: an indicator obtained from lichens. Used as a solution or impregnated into paper (litmus paper), which is dampened before use. Litmus turns red under acid conditions and purple in alkaline conditions. Litmus is a crude indicator when compared with Universal Indicator.

load (electronics): an impedance or circuit that receives or develops the output of a cell or other power supply.

lustre: the shininess of a substance.

malleable: able to be pressed or hammered into shape.

manometer: a device for measuring gas pressure. A simple manometer is made by partly filling a U-shaped rubber tube with water and connecting one end to the source of gas whose pressure is to be measured. The pressure is always relative to atmospheric pressure.

mass: the amount of matter in an object. In everyday use the word weight is often used (somewhat incorrectly) to mean mass.

matter: anything that has mass and takes up space.

melting point: the temperature at which a substance changes state from a solid phase to a liquid phase. It is the same as freezing point.

membrane: a thin, flexible sheet. A semipermeable membrane has microscopic holes of a size that will selectively allow some ions and molecules to pass through but hold others back. It thus acts as a kind of filter. *Example:* a membrane used for osmosis.

meniscus: the curved surface of a liquid that forms in a small bore or capillary tube. The meniscus is convex (bulges upwards) for mercury and is concave (sags downwards) for water.

metal: a class of elements that is a good conductor of electricity and heat, has a metallic lustre, is malleable and ductile, forms cations and has oxides that are bases. Metals are formed as cations

held together by a sea of electrons. A metal may also be an alloy of these elements. *Example:* sodium, calcium, gold. *See:* alloy, metalloid, non-metal.

metallic bonding: cations reside in a 'sea' of mobile electrons. It allows metals to be good conductors and means that they are not brittle. *See:* bonding.

metallic lustre: *See:* lustre.

metalloid: a class of elements intermediate in properties between metals and non-metals. Metalloids are also called semi-metals or semiconductors. *Example:* silicon, germanium, antimony. *See:* metal, non-metal, semiconductor.

micronutrient: an element that the body requires in small amounts. Another term is trace element.

mineral: a solid substance made of just one element or compound. *Example:* calcite is a mineral because it consists only of calcium carbonate; halite is a mineral because it contains only sodium chloride.

mineral acid: an acid that does not contain carbon and which attacks minerals. Hydrochloric, sulphuric and nitric acids are the main mineral acids.

miscible: capable of being mixed.

mixing combustion: the form of combustion that occurs when two gases thoroughly mix before they ignite and so produce almost complete combustion. *Example:* when a Bunsen flame is blue.

mixture: a material that can be separated into two or more substances using physical means. *Example:* a mixture of copper(II) sulphate and cadmium sulphide can be separated by filtration.

molar mass: the mass per mole of atoms of an element. It has the same value and uses the same units as atomic weight. *Example:* molar mass of chlorine is 35.45 g/mol. *See:* atomic weight.

mole: 1 mole is the amount of a substance which contains Avagadro's number (6×10^{23}) of particles. *Example:* 1 mole of carbon-12 weighs exactly 12 g.

molecular mass: *See:* molar mass.

molecular weight: *See:* molar mass.

molecule: a group of two or more atoms held together by chemical bonds. *Example:* O_2.

monoclinic system: a grouping of crystals that look like double-ended chisel blades.

monomer: a small molecule and building block for larger chain molecules or polymers ('mono' means one, 'mer' means part). *Examples:* tetrafluoroethene for teflon, ethene for polyethene.

native element: an element that occurs in an uncombined state. *Examples:* sulphur, gold.

native metal: a pure form of a metal, not combined as a compound. Native metal is more common in poorly reactive elements than in those that are very reactive. *Examples:* copper, gold.

net ionic reaction: the overall, or net, change that occurs in a reaction, seen in terms of ions.

neutralisation: the reaction of acids and bases to produce a salt and water. The reaction causes hydrogen from the acid and hydroxide from the base to be changed to water. *Example:* hydrochloric acid reacts with, and neutralises, sodium hydroxide to form the salt sodium chloride (common salt) and water. The term is more generally used for any reaction in which the pH changes toward 7.0, which is the pH of a neutral solution. *See:* pH.

neutralisation point: *See:* end point.

neutron: a particle inside the nucleus of an atom that is neutral and has no charge.

newton (N): the unit of force required to give one kilogram an acceleration of one metre per second every second ($1\ ms^{-2}$).

nitrate: a compound that includes nitrogen and oxygen and contains more oxygen than a nitrite. Nitrate ions have the chemical formula NO_3^-. *Examples:* sodium nitrate $NaNO_3$ and lead nitrate $Pb(NO_3)_2$.

nitrite: a compound that includes nitrogen and oxygen and contains less oxygen than a nitrate. Nitrite ions have the chemical formula NO_2^-. *Example:* sodium nitrite $NaNO_2$.

noble gases: the members of Group 8 of the Periodic Table: helium, neon, argon, krypton, xenon, radon. These gases are almost entirely unreactive.

noble metals: silver, gold, platinum and mercury. These are the least reactive metals.

non-combustible: a substance that will not combust or burn. *Example:* carbon dioxide.

non-metal: a brittle substance that does not conduct electricity. *Examples:* sulphur, phosphorus, all gases. *See:* metal, metalloid.

normal salt: salts that do not contain a hydroxide (OH^-) ion, which would make them basic salts, or a hydrogen ion, which would make them acid salts. *Example:* sodium chloride (NaCl).

nucleus: the small, positively charged particle at the centre of an atom. The nucleus is responsible for most of the mass of an atom.

opaque: a substance that will not transmit light so that it is impossible to see through it. Most solids are opaque.

ore: a rock containing enough of a useful substance to make mining it worthwhile. *Example:* bauxite, aluminium ore.

organic acid: an acid containing carbon and hydrogen. *Example:* methanoic (formic) acid (HCOOH).

organic chemistry: the study of organic compounds.

organic compound (organic substance; organic material): a compound (or substance) that contains carbon and usually hydrogen. (The carbonates are usually excluded.) *Examples:* methane (CH_4), chloromethane (CH_3Cl), ethene (C_2H_4), ethanol (C_2H_5OH), ethanoic acid (C_2H_3OOH), etc.

organic solvent: an organic substance that will dissolve other substances. *Example:* carbon tetrachloride (CCl_4).

osmosis: a process whereby molecules of a liquid solvent move through a semipermeable membrane from a region of low concentration of a solute to a region with a high concentration of a solute.

oxidation–reduction reaction (redox reaction): reaction in which oxidation and reduction occurs; a reaction in which electrons are transferred. *Example:* copper and oxygen react to produce copper(II) oxide. The copper is oxidised, and oxygen is reduced.

oxidation: combination with oxygen or a reaction in which an atom, ion or molecule loses electrons to an oxidising agent. (Note that an oxidising agent does not have to contain oxygen.) The opposite of oxidation is reduction. *See:* reduction.

oxidation number (oxidation state): the effective charge on an atom in a compound. An increase in oxidation number corresponds to oxidation, and a decrease to reduction. Shown in Roman numerals. *Example:* manganate(IV).

oxidation state: *See:* oxidation number.

oxide: a compound that includes oxygen and one other element. *Example:* copper oxide (CuO).

oxidise: to combine with or gain oxygen or to react such that an atom, ion or molecule loses electrons to an oxidising agent.

oxidising agent: a substance that removes electrons from another substance being oxidised (and therefore is itself reduced) in a redox reaction. *Example:* chlorine (Cl_2).

ozone: a form of oxygen whose molecules contain three atoms of oxygen. Ozone is regarded as a beneficial gas when high in the atmosphere because it blocks ultraviolet rays. It is a harmful gas when breathed in, so low level ozone which is produced as part of city smog is regarded as a form of pollution. The ozone layer is the uppermost part of the stratosphere.

partial pressure: the pressure a gas in a mixture would exert if it alone occupied a flask. *Example:* oxygen makes up about a fifth of the atmosphere. Its partial pressure is therefore about a fifth of normal atmospheric pressure.

pascal: the unit of pressure, equal to one newton per square metre of surface. *See:* newton.

patina: a surface coating that develops on metals and protects them from further corrosion. *Example:* the green coating of copper carbonate that forms on copper statues.

percolate: to move slowly through the pores of a rock.

period: a row in the Periodic Table.

Periodic Table: a chart organising elements by atomic number and chemical properties into groups and periods.

pestle and mortar: a pestle is a ceramic rod with a rounded end, a mortar is a ceramic dish. Pestle and mortar are used together to pound or grind solids into fine powders.

Petri dish: a shallow glass or plastic dish with a lid.

petroleum: a natural mixture of a range of gases, liquids and solids derived from the decomposed remains of plants and animals.

pH: a measure of the hydrogen ion concentration in a liquid. Neutral is pH 7.0; numbers greater than this are alkaline; smaller numbers are acidic. *See:* neutralisation, acid, base.

pH meter: a device that accurately measures the pH of a solution. A pH meter is a voltmeter that measures the electric potential difference between two electrodes (which are attached to the meter through a probe) when they are submerged in a solution. The readings are shown on a dial or digital display.

phase: a particular state of matter. A substance may exist as a solid, liquid or gas and may change between these phases with addition or removal of energy. *Examples:* ice, liquid and vapour are the three phases of water. Ice undergoes a phase change to water when heat energy is added.

phosphor: any material that glows when energised by ultraviolet or electron beams, such as in fluorescent tubes and cathode ray tubes. Phosphors, such as phosphorus, emit light after the source of excitation is cut off. This is why they glow in the dark. By contrast, fluorescers, such as fluorite, only emit light while they are being excited by ultraviolet light or an electron beam.

photochemical smog: photochemical reactions are caused by the energy of sunlight. Photochemical smog is a mixture of tiny particles and a brown haze caused by the reaction of colourless nitric oxide from vehicle exhausts and oxygen of the air to form brown nitrogen dioxide.

photon: a parcel of light energy.

photosynthesis: the process by which plants use the energy of the Sun to make the compounds they need for life. In photosynthesis, six molecules of carbon dioxide from the air combine with six molecules of water, forming one molecule of glucose (sugar) and releasing six molecules of oxygen back into the atmosphere.

pipe-clay triangle: a device made from three small pieces of ceramic tube which are wired together in the shape of a triangle. Pipe-clay triangles are used to support round-bottomed dishes when they are heated in a Bunsen flame.

pipette: a log, slender, glass tube used, in conjunction with a pipette filler, to draw up and then transfer accurately measured amounts of liquid.

plastic: (material) a carbon-based substance consisting of long chains (polymers) of simple molecules. The word plastic is commonly restricted to synthetic polymers. *Examples:* polyvinyl chloride, nylon: **(property)** a material is plastic if it can be made to change shape easily. Plastic materials will remain in the new shape. (Compare with elastic, a property whereby a material goes back to its original shape.)

pneumatic trough: a shallow water-filled glass dish used to house a beehive shelf and a gas jar as part of the apparatus for collecting a gas over water.

polar solvent: a solvent in which the atoms have partial electric charges. *Example:* water.

polymer: a compound that is made of long chains by combining molecules (called monomers) as repeating units. ('Poly' means many, 'mer' means part.) *Examples:* polytetrafluoroethene or Teflon from tetrafluoroethene, Terylene from terephthalic acid and ethane-1,2-diol (ethylene glycol).

polymerisation: a chemical reaction in which large numbers of similar molecules arrange themselves into large molecules, usually long chains. This process usually happens when there is a suitable catalyst present. *Example:* ethene gas reacts to form polyethene in the presence of certain catalysts.

polymorphism: (meaning many shapes) the tendency of some materials to have more than one solid form. *Example:* carbon as diamond, graphite and buckminsterfullerene.

porous: a material containing many small holes or cracks. Quite often the pores are connected, and liquids, such as water or oil, can move through them.

potential difference: a measure of the work that must be done to move an electric charge from one point to the other in a circuit. Potential difference is measured in volts, V. *See:* electrical potential.

precious metal: silver, gold, platinum, iridium and palladium. Each is prized for its rarity.

precipitate: a solid substance formed as a result of a chemical reaction between two liquids or gases. *Example:* iron(III) hydroxide is precipitated when sodium hydroxide solution is added to iron(III) chloride. *See:* gelatinous precipitate, granular precipitate.

preservative: a substance that prevents the natural organic decay processes from occurring. Many substances can be used safely for this purpose, including sulphites and nitrogen gas.

pressure: the force per unit area measured in pascals. *See:* pascal, atmospheric pressure.

product: a substance produced by a chemical reaction. *Example:* when the reactants copper and oxygen react, they produce the product, copper oxide.

proton: a positively charged particle in the nucleus of an atom that balances out the charge of the surrounding electrons.

proton number: this is the modern expression for atomic number. *See:* atomic number.

purify: to remove all impurities from a mixture, perhaps by precipitation, or filtration.

pyrolysis: chemical decomposition brought about by heat. *Example:* decomposition of lead nitrate. *See:* destructive distillation.

pyrometallurgy: refining a metal from its ore using heat. A blast furnace or smelter is the main equipment used.

quantitative: measurement of the amounts of constituents of a substance, for example by mass or volume. *See:* gravimetric analysis, volumetric analysis.

radiation: the exchange of energy with the surroundings through the transmission of waves or particles of energy. Radiation is a form of energy transfer that can happen through space; no intervening medium is required (as would be the case for conduction and convection).

radical: an atom, molecule, or ion with at least one unpaired electron. *Example:* nitrogen monoxide (NO).

radioactive: emitting radiation or particles from the nucleus of its atoms.

radioactive decay: a change in a radioactive element due to loss of mass through radiation. For example, uranium decays (changes) to lead.

reactant: a starting material that takes part in, and undergoes, change during a chemical reaction. *Example:* hydrochloric acid and calcium carbonate are reactants; the reaction produces the products calcium chloride, carbon dioxide and water.

reaction: the recombination of two substances using parts of each substance to produce new substances. *Example:* the reactants sodium chloride and sulphuric acid react and recombine to form the products sodium sulphate, chlorine and water.

reactivity: the tendency of a substance to react with other substances. The term is most widely used in comparing the reactivity of metals. Metals are arranged in a reactivity series.

reactivity series: the series of metals organised in order of their reactivity, with the most reactive metals, such as sodium, at the top and the least react metals, such as gold, at the bottom. Hydrogen is usually included in the series for comparative purposes.

reagent: a commonly available substance (reactant) used to create a reaction. Reagents are the chemicals normally kept on chemistry laboratory benches. Many substances called reagents are most commonly used for test purposes.

redox reaction (oxidation–reduction reaction): a reaction that involves oxidation and reduction; a reactions in which electrons are transferred. *See:* oxidation–reduction.

reducing agent: a substance that gives electrons to another substance being reduced (and therefore itself being oxidised) in a redox reaction. *Example:* hydrogen sulphide (H_2S).

reduction: the removal of oxygen from, or the addition of hydrogen

to, a compound. Also a reaction in which an atom, ion or molecule gains electrons from an reducing agent. (The opposite of reduction is oxidation.)

reduction tube: a boiling tube with a small hole near the closed end. The tube is mounted horizontally, a sample is placed in the tube and a reducing gas, such as carbon monoxide, is passed through the tube. The oxidised gas escapes through the small hole.

refining: separating a mixture into the simpler substances of which it is made.

reflux distillation system: a form of distillation using a Liebig condenser placed vertically, so that all the vapours created during boiling are condensed back into the liquid, rather than escaping. In this way, the concentration of all the reactants remains constant.

relative atomic mass: in the past a measure of the mass of an atom on a scale relative to the mass of an atom of hydrogen, where hydrogen is 1. Nowadays a measure of the mass of an atom relative to the mass of one twelfth of an atom of carbon-12. If the relative atomic mass is given as a rounded figure, it is called an approximate relative atomic mass. *Examples:* chlorine 35, calcium 40, gold 197. *See:* atomic mass, atomic weight.

reversible reaction: a reaction in which the products can be transformed back into their original chemical form. *Example:* heated iron reacts with steam to produce iron oxide and hydrogen. If the hydrogen is passed over this heated oxide, it forms iron and steam. $3Fe + 4H_2O \rightleftharpoons Fe_3O_4 + 4H_2$.

roast: heating a substance for a long time at a high temperature, as in a furnace.

rust: the product of the corrosion of iron and steel in the presence of air and water.

salt: a compound, often involving a metal, that is the reaction product of an acid and a base, or of two elements. (Note 'salt' is also the common word for sodium chloride, common salt or table salt.) *Example:* sodium chloride (NaCl) and potassium sulphate (K_2SO_4) *See:* acid salt, basic salt, normal salt.

salt bridge: a permeable material soaked in a salt solution that allows ions to be transferred from one container to another. The salt solution remains unchanged during this transfer. *Example:* sodium sulphate used as a salt bridge in a galvanic cell.

saponification: a reaction between a fat and a base that produces a soap.

saturated: a state in which a liquid can hold no more of a substance. If any more of the substance is added, it will not dissolve.

saturated hydrocarbon: a hydrocarbon in which the carbon atoms are held with single bonds. *Example:* ethane (C_2H_6).

saturated solution: a solution that holds the maximum possible amount of dissolved material. When saturated, the rate of dissolving solid and that of recrystallisation solid are the same, and a condition of equilibrium is reached. The amount of material in solution varies with the temperature; cold solutions can hold less dissolved solid material than hot solutions. Gases are more soluble in cold liquids than in hot liquids.

sediment: material that settles out at the bottom of a liquid when it is still. A precipitate is one form of sediment.

semiconductor: a material of intermediate conductivity. Semiconductor devices often use silicon when they are made as part of diodes, transistors or integrated circuits. Elements intermediate between metals and non-metals

are also sometimes called semiconductors. *Example:* germanium oxide, germanium. *See:* metalloid.

semipermeable membrane: a thin material that acts as a fine sieve or filter, allowing small molecules to pass, but holding large molecules back.

separating column: used in chromatography. A tall glass tube containing a porous disc near the base and filled with a substance (for example, aluminium oxide, which is known as a stationary phase) that can adsorb materials on its surface. When a mixture is passed through the column, fractions are retarded by differing amounts, so that each fraction is washed through the column in sequence.

separating funnel: a pear-shaped, glassware funnel designed to permit the separation of immiscible liquids by simply pouring off the more dense liquid while leaving the less dense liquid in the funnel.

series circuit: an electrical circuit in which all of the components are joined end to end in a line.

shell: the term used to describe the imaginary ball-shaped surface outside the nucleus of an atom that would be formed by a set of electrons of similar energy. The outermost shell is known as the valence shell. *Example:* neon has shells containing 2 and 8 electrons.

side-arm boiling tube: a boiling tube with an integral glass pipe near its open end. The side arm is normally used for the entry or exit of a gas.

simple distillation: the distillation of a substance when only one volatile fraction is to be collected. Simple distillation uses a Liebig condenser arranged almost horizontally. When the liquid mixture is heated and vapours are produced, they enter the

condenser and then flow away from the flask and can be collected. *Example:* simple distillation of ethanoic acid.

slag: a mixture of substances that are waste products of a furnace. Most slags are composed mainly of silicates.

smelting: roasting a substance in order to extract the metal contained in it.

smog: a mixture of smoke and fog. The term is used to describe city fogs in which there is a large proportion of particulate matter (tiny pieces of carbon from exhausts) and also a high concentration of sulphur and nitrogen gases and probably ozone. *See:* photochemical smog.

smokeless fuel: a fuel which has been subjected to partial pyrolysis, such that there is no more loose particulate matter remaining. *Example:* Coke is a smokeless fuel.

solid/solid phase: a rigid form of matter which maintains its shape, whatever its container.

solubility: the maximum amount of a substance that can be contained in a solvent.

soluble: readily dissolvable in a solvent.

solute: a substance that has dissolved. *Example:* sodium chloride in water.

solution: a mixture of a liquid (the solvent) and at least one other substance of lesser abundance (the solute). Mixtures can be separated by physical means, for example, by evaporation and cooling. *See:* aqueous solution.

solvent: the main substance in a solution.

spectator ions: the ionic part of a compound that does not play an active part in a reaction. *Example:* when magnesium ribbon is placed in copper(II) sulphate solution, the copper is displaced from the solution by the magnesium, while the sulphate ion (SO_4^{2-}) plays no part in the reaction and so behaves as a spectator ion.

spectrum: a progressive series arranged using a characteristic etc. *Examples:* the range of colours that make up visible light (as seen in a rainbow) or across all electromagnetic radiation, arranged in progression according to their wavelength.

spontaneous combustion: the effect of a very reactive material or combination of reactants that suddenly reach their ignition temperature and begin to combust rapidly.

standard temperature and pressure (STP): 0°C at one atmosphere (a pressure which supports a column of mercury 760 mm high). Also given as 0°C at 100 kilopascals. *See:* atmospheric pressure.

state of matter: the physical form of matter. There are three states of matter: liquid, solid and gaseous.

stationary phase: a name given to a material which is used as a medium for separating a liquid mixture in chromatography.

strong acid: an acid that has completely dissociated (ionised) in water. Mineral acids are strong acids.

sublime/sublimation: the change of a substance from solid to gas, or vice versa, without going through a liquid phase. *Example:* iodine sublimes from a purple solid to a purple gas.

substance: a type of material, including mixtures.

sulphate: a compound that includes sulphur and oxygen and contains more oxygen than a sulphite. Sulphate ions have the chemical formula SO_4^{2-}. *Examples:* calcium sulphate $CaSO_4$ (the main

constituent of gypsum) and aluminium sulphate $Al_2(SO_4)_3$ (an alum).

sulphide: a sulphur compound that contains no oxygen. Sulphide ions have the chemical formula S^{2-}. *Example:* hydrogen sulphide (H_2S).

sulphite: a compound that includes sulphur and oxygen but contains less oxygen than a sulphate. Sulphite ions have the chemical formula SO_3^{2-}. *Example:* sodium sulphite Na_2SO_3.

supercooling: the ability of some substances to cool below their normal freezing point. *Example:* sodium thiosulphate.

supersaturated solution: a solution in which the amount of solute is greater than that which would normally be expected in a saturated solution. Most solids are more soluble in hot solutions than in cold. If a hot saturated solution is made up, the solution can be rapidly cooled down below its freezing point before it begins to solidify. This is a supersaturated solution.

surface tension: the force that operates on the surface of a liquid and which makes it act as though it were covered with an invisible, elastic film.

suspension: a mist of tiny particles in a liquid.

synthesis: a reaction in which a substance is formed from simpler reactants. *Example:* hydrogen gas and chlorine gas react to sythesise hydrogen chloride gas. The term can also be applied to polymerisation of organic compounds.

synthetic: does not occur naturally but has to be manufactured. Commonly used in the name 'synthetic fibre'.

tare: an allowance made for the weight of a container.

tarnish: a coating that develops as a result of the reaction between a metal and substances in the air. The most common form of tarnishing is a very thin, transparent oxide coating.

terminal: one of the electrodes of a battery.

test (chemical): a reagent or a procedure used to reveal the presence of another reagent. *Example:* litmus and other indicators are used to test the acidity or alkalinity of a substance.

test tube: A thin, glass tube, closed at one end and used for chemical tests, etc. The composition and thickness of the glass is such that, while it is inert to most chemical reactions, it may not sustain very high temperatures but can usually be heated in a Bunsen flame. *See:* boiling tube.

thermal decomposition: the breakdown of a substance using heat. *See* pyrolysis.

thermoplastic: a plastic that will soften and can be moulded repeatedly into shape on heating and will set into the moulded shape as it cools.

thermoset: a plastic that will set into a moulded shape as it cools, but which cannot be made soft by reheating.

thistle funnel: a narrow tube, expanded at the top into a thistlehead-shaped vessel. It is used as a funnel when introducing small amounts of liquid reactant. When fitted with a tap, it can be used to control the rate of entry of a reactant. *See:* burette.

titration: the analysis of the composition of a substance in a solution by measuring the volume of that solution (the titrant, normally in a burette) needed to react with a given volume of another solution (the titrate, normally placed in a flask). An indicator is often used to signal

change. *Example:* neutralisation of sodium hydroxide using hydrochloric acid in an acid–base titration. *See:* end point.

toxic: poisonous.

transition metals: the group of metals that belong to the d-block of the Periodic Table. Transition metals commonly have a number of differently coloured oxidation states. *Examples:* iron, vanadium.

Universal Indicator: a mixture of indicators commonly used in the laboratory because of its reliability. Used as a solution or impregnated into paper (Indicator paper), which is dampened before use. Universal Indicator changes colour from purple in a strongly alkaline solution through green when the solution is neutral to red in strongly acidic solutions. Universal Indicator is more accurate than litmus paper but less accurate than a pH meter.

unsaturated hydrocarbon: a hydrocarbon, in which at least one bond is a double or triple bond. Hydrogen atoms can be added to unsaturated compounds to form saturated compounds. *Example:* ethene, C_2H_4 or $CH_2=CH_2$.

vacuum: a container from which air has been removed using a pump.

valency: the number of bonds that an atom can form. *Examples:* calcium has a valency of 2 and bromine a valency of 1

valency shell: the outermost shell of an atom. *See:* shell.

vapour: the gaseous phase of a substance that is a liquid or a solid at that temperature. *Examples:* water vapour is the gaseous form of water, iodine vapour is the gaseous form of solid iodine. *See:* gas.

vein: a fissure in rock that has filled with ore or other mineral-bearing rock.

viscous: slow-moving, syrupy. A liquid that has a low viscosity is said to be mobile.

volatile: readily forms a gas.

volatile fraction: the part of a liquid mixture that will vaporise readily under the conditions prevailing during the reaction. *See:* fraction, vapour.

water of crystallisation: the water molecules absorbed into the crystalline structure as a liquid changes to a solid. *Example:* hydrated copper(II) sulphate $CuSO_4 \cdot 5H_2O$. *See:* hydrate.

weak acid and **weak base**: an acid or base that has only partly dissociated (ionised) in water. Most organic acids are weak acids. *See:* organic acid.

weight: the gravitational force on a substance. *See:* mass.

X-rays: a form of very short wave radiation.

MASTER INDEX